THE
GREAT BRITISH
ROYAL FAMILY
QUIZ BOOK

For Mum and Dad

THE GREAT BRITISH ROYAL FAMILY QUIZ BOOK

ONE'S TOUGHEST QUESTIONS AND THEIR ANSWERS

Daniel Smith

greenfinch

CONTENTS

JUST LIKE THE REST OF US

PRIVATE LIVES

FACTS AND FIGURES

ANSWERS

INTRODUCTION

The institution of the British monarchy is living on borrowed time. It costs too much and gives back too little. Its political power is merely illusory and its leading personnel distant and out of touch. When all is said and done, the royal family is an anachronism, unsuited for the modern world.

These are a few of the lines that certain commentators would have us believe. Worst of all, they tell us, the public no longer believes in the Crown. And yet...

Rather like those people who march up and down high streets wearing sandwich boards warning the rest of us that the end is nigh, there have been generations of doommongers predicting the demise of the royal family. They said it when Bad King John was facing the wrath of the barons, and when Henry VIII's sole male heir perished (which, it of course turned out, actually heralded the glories of the first Elizabethan age), and when George III lost the Americas, and then when Victoria hid herself away from the public to deal with her personal grief. Most spectacularly, it really did seem like the game was up for the monarchy when King Charles I was forcibly separated from his head in 1649, only for the public to decide that they did not much like the alternative and so offered the Crown back to his son a little over a decade later. To paraphrase Mark Twain, reports of the death of the monarchy have been exaggerated for a long time now.

Queen Elizabeth II is now history's most enduring manifestation of the institution. She has graced the throne in no less than eight decades, outlasting cold wars and hot wars, booms and recessions, Britain's stormy entry into, and equally stormy exit from, the European Union. She has, to date, said hello and goodbye to 14 prime ministers, witnessed the demise of old industries and the emergence of new ones, been an integral part of the rise of television, seen glorious moments of sporting glory and the hosting of the Olympic Games, and watched on as the rural and urban landscapes of her realm have changed sometimes beyond recognition. Not to mention that she has lived through myriad personal and family crises that might have brought down a lesser character. And still she remains, steadfast, true and as committed to her duties as she ever was.

It is little wonder, then, that she and, by and large, her family continue to garner enormous popularity. Let it not be forgotten, either, that for the first decade of her life Elizabeth never expected to have to bear the onerous responsibilities of sovereignty. Only with her uncle's abdication when she was ten years old did her father unexpectedly find himself king and Elizabeth the heir to the throne. Heavy is the head that

wears the crown, so says the maxim. But she has worn it with style and assuredness. She has never failed to rise to the challenge of monarchy, putting public duty ahead of all other considerations.

To the undoubted disappointment of several generations of republicans by now, her confident captaining of the royal ship has ensured that the institution remains relevant to the wider world. When she makes her annual Christmas address to the people of Britain and the Commonwealth, tens of millions tune in to listen. At moments of true national crisis, her government has sought her steadying hand to calm the collective jangling nerves. And whenever there is a royal celebration – a jubilee, a wedding or the arrival of a new member of the family – it is guaranteed to raise the nation's spirits.

It is not merely permissible, but indeed rather healthy to question the institution of monarchy: to consider whether or not it is working to reflect the modern world; to wonder if it spends its money in the most publicly beneficial ways; to raise an eyebrow when some or other individual member of the family missteps either in public or private. We rightly do not owe the monarchy the sort of unquestioning loyalty and devotion that kings and queens of yore demanded (with suitably frightening punishments for those who refused). In other words, we have the right not to like the royal family, to consider it immaterial to our everyday lives, to ignore it. And while a few take up those rights with gusto, what is perhaps more striking is how many more retain not merely respect, but genuine affection for the monarchy.

See the snaking queues of those who want to catch a glimpse of the interior of Buckingham Palace or Windsor

Castle. Consider the billions who tune in to a royal wedding given half a chance. Study the spikes in newspaper circulations and online views for stories that focus on the royals, proving our insatiable appetite for regal gossip and drama every bit as much as all the pomp and ceremony stuff. Take a look around any number of family homes and you'll likely spot a commemorative plate or mug of more recent vintage than you'd perhaps expect. Whatever the naysayers might have you believe, the royal family remains an integral and vital part of our social fabric.

Perhaps the Crown's greatest trick is to appear so constant and unchanging while in fact being remarkably adaptable. Elizabeth II has been a touchstone of steadfastness, yet she has also overseen vast changes in the institution she heads. Despite regular charges of being stuck in the past, the royal family has a canny knack of adjusting to meet each new challenge and demand it faces. The institution that Elizabeth will eventually pass on will look vastly different not only from that of, say, the court of Henry VIII, but even from the one bequeathed her by her own father. The royal family: timeless yet dynamic.

This quiz book, then, is an unapologetic celebration of that family. A chance for you to test your knowledge of all things royal, but also to immerse yourself in regal trivia that may have passed you by or else been filed so deep in the recesses of your memory that you have forgotten it is even there. While many of the questions focus on the royal family of today, there is plenty for history buffs, too. From suspicious deaths in the medieval age to the Queen's middle names and the auction price achieved by Princess Beatrice's hat, there is something for everyone. Read on for a true royal tournament of the mind!

POMP
AND
CEREMONY

There is nothing to set the pulse racing like the pomp and ceremony that surrounds the British royal family. There are, of course, other royal families around the world but none of them have retained that sense of history, tradition and, let's be honest about it, commitment to bling that the Windsors have managed to maintain. Who can fail to be awestruck by a royal home such as Buckingham Palace or Windsor Castle? Or with royal treasures including everything from jewels the size of a child's fist to masterworks from some of the greatest artists and craftsmen ever to tread this Earth? Not to mention the sheer theatricality of a royal occasion, replete with heart-stirring music and compelling (if sometimes baffling) protocols. In this section, then, you will find quizzes on royal abodes, treasures and works of art, along with further quizzes on royal fashion and regal protocol.

CROWNING GLORIES: ROYAL TREASURES

When it comes to bling, there's still no one to touch the royal family. From the Crown Jewels to the Royal Collection of art, how much do you know about their treasures and trinkets?

Answers, pages 148–49

1. The Crown Jewels are on public display in a specially designed jewel house at which London landmark?

2. Queen Mary's Doll's House, originally exhibited at the British Empire Exhibition during 1924–25 and seen by more than 1.5 million people, was designed by which noted architect?

3. A special miniature library of almost 600 volumes was created for the doll's house, but which of the following authors declined to submit an original story?

   A: George Bernard Shaw
   B: Rudyard Kipling
   C: Sir Arthur Conan Doyle

4. The Crown Jewels are made up of over 140 distinct items. The collection incorporates approximately how many precious stones?

   A: 11,000
   D. 17,000
   C: 23,000

5. Arguably the most significant item in the Crown Jewels is St Edward's Crown. For whose coronation was the crown made?

St Edward's Crown is made of solid gold, inset with 440 gemstones and weighs 2.25kg (5lb) – truly, heavy is the head that wears the crown. The Queen hasn't worn it since her coronation, opting instead for the lighter Imperial State Crown for official occasions, such as the State Opening of Parliament.

6. George V and Queen Mary collected three magnificent ornamental eggs by which celebrated jeweller?

7. George IV commissioned a painting of the Battle of Trafalgar that caused controversy on its completion in 1824 for its perceived historical inaccuracies. Who was the artist?

8. Who gave the Queen a wedding present of a piece of cotton lace that they had spun themselves?

9. Which historically important artefact, weighing around 152kg (335lb) and used during coronations, was relocated to Edinburgh Castle from Westminster Abbey after 700 years in London?

10. Only three individuals are permitted to touch St Edward's Crown with ungloved hands. The Queen and the Crown Jeweller are two of them, but who is the third?

11. What is the name of the world-famous 105-carat diamond – once part of the legendary Mughal Peacock Throne and now set in the Queen Mother's Crown – that reputedly brings bad luck to any man who wears it?

12. At the end of the English Civil War in the early 1660s, Oliver Cromwell's government melted down the Crown Jewels of Charles I and used the metal to create a statue of Cromwell as Lord Protector. True or false?

13. The Royal Collection, the world's largest private art collection, includes roughly how many paintings?

    A: 2,500
    B: 5,500
    C: 17,500

14. The Royal Collection also includes an extraordinary collection of some 600 drawings, including virtually all the surviving anatomical drawings, of which Renaissance artist?

15. In 1972 the Queen was given what gift by the government of Cameroon?

    A: a lion called Lenny
    B: a rhino called Grumpy
    C: an elephant called Jumbo

16. After Edward VIII abdicated and left Britain for Europe, he took some of the Crown Jewels with him. True or false?

17. What was the name of the man who led an audacious bid to steal the Crown Jewels in 1671?

18. In 2017, Mark Appleby was given which prestigious appointment?

19. The Crown Jewels include a sceptre adorned with the largest clear-cut diamond in the world at over 530 carats. By what name is the gem known?

> Discovered in 1905 in the Transvaal Colony in South Africa, the diamond described in question 19 went unsold for two years before the Transvaal government purchased it and gifted it to Edward VII. To put off would-be robbers, a decoy stone was sent to England aboard a ship while the real diamond was delivered using the postal system.

20. In 2013, on a state visit to the Kingdom of Jordan, Prince Charles was presented with a ceramic figure of himself alongside which popular cartoon character?

A: Noddy
B: Postman Pat
C: Bob the Builder

ONE'S HOME IS
ONE'S CASTLE:
ROYAL HOMES

One thing members of the royal family don't have
to worry about is keeping a roof over their heads.
How much can you recall about their many
properties, spread throughout the kingdom.

Answers, pages 150–51

1. Hampton Court Palace was gifted to the English monarchy in the 16th century by which famous cardinal and Lord Chancellor?

2. During the First World War, George V saw to it that Buckingham Palace's wine cellars were locked in the interests of setting a good example to the lower orders. True or false?

3. What is the name of the Queen's official residence in Northern Ireland?

4. What flag flies above Buckingham Palace when the Queen is in residence?

5. Buckingham Palace was originally known as Buckingham House when it was constructed in the early 18th century. Which monarch purchased it from its owner, the Duke of Buckingham?

Buckingham House was built in 1703 to serve as a townhouse for the Duke of Buckingham. William Winde was responsible for the original design but it underwent a significant facelift after it came into royal ownership – most notably under the guidance of the architects John Nash and, later, Edward Blore.

6. How did Michael Fagan shoot to infamy in 1982?

7. Which royal has leased the Mansion House at Bagshot Park, Surrey, from the Crown Estate since 1998?

A: Prince Edward
B: Prince Andrew
C: Zara Tindall (née Phillips)

8. How many rooms does Buckingham Palace contain?

A: 275
B: 575
C: 775

9. Who was the last monarch to have taken permanent residence in Scotland?

10. From which notable political and publishing family did the Duchy of Cornwall purchase the Highgrove estate in Gloucestershire in 1980?

11. Following a devastating fire in 1992, what was the estimated cost of the repairs to Windsor Castle?

A: £10 million
B: £40 million
C: £90 million

12. What is the current name of the royal residence once known as Nottingham House after it was purchased by the first Earl of Nottingham in 1619?

13. A 4.3-metre-high (14-ft) statue made by Sir George Frampton can be found in Kensington Gardens, one of London's royal parks. Which literary character does it depict?

14. Llwynywermod is the unassuming Welsh home of which royal couple?

15. How much money did the Duke and Duchess of Sussex receive as a Sovereign Grant for the renovations to their Windsor home, Frogmore Cottage?

A: £2.4 million
B: £4.8 million
C: £7.2 million

16. Tamarisk, a 1960s-built brick house belonging to the Prince of Wales, is located on which archipelago?

17. What is the name of Princess Anne's Gloucestershire residence, the grounds of which host an annual international horse trials?

The palace referred to in question 19 was originally an Augustinian abbey built in 1128. Mary, Queen of Scots was one of its residents, and her time there was never less than dramatic. As well as marrying twice within the palace, she also saw her private secretary David Rizzio murdered there in 1566 by her second husband, Lord Darnley. Almost two centuries later and Bonnie Prince Charlie moved in to the palace after he had laid claim to Edinburgh during the Jacobite rebellion.

18. Which royal residence has appeared on the reverse side of £100 notes since 1987?

19. The Palace of Holyroodhouse, sits at the lower end of which famous thoroughfare?

20. What was the name of the run-down Scottish castle bought by Queen Elizabeth, the Queen Mother in 1952, which she subsequently restored and renamed?

WHO WORE
WHAT, WHERE?
ROYAL FASHION

It goes without saying that we expect our royals
to be well presented at all times. But straddling
the line between timeless elegance and high
fashion can be tricky. How much do you
know about royal style past and present?

Answers, pages 152–53

1. Sarah Burton designed the Duchess of Cambridge's wedding dress in 2011, but which fashion house does she represent?

2. The company Cornelia James provides the Queen with which item of attire?

3. Which once close friend of the Prince Regent (later George IV) was the most famous dandy in Regency England – a man whose fame rested in large part on his sartorial elegance?

4. According to royal protocol, what status ought a woman to have before she can wear a tiara?

5. The husband-and-wife team of David and Elizabeth Emanuel designed Princess Anne's dress for her wedding to Captain Mark Phillips. True or false?

6. The Philip Treacy designed hat that Princess Beatrice wore to the wedding of the Duke and Duchess of Cambridge was subsequently auctioned for charity. How much did it sell for?

   A: £11,100.01
   B: £51,100.01
   C: £81,100.01

7. What colour of spare outfit do royals routinely take with them on foreign trips for use in an emergency?

8. Which French-born fashion designer supplied over a thousand outfits to Princess Diana, including the iconic 'Elvis gown' that she wore in 1989 to the British Fashion Awards and then on an official trip to Hong Kong?

9. Wallis Simpson's attire for her wedding in 1937 to the Duke of Windsor caused a sensation, with a hue even being named in the bride's honour. By what name did the shade she wore come to be known?

10. Why did the Queen's choice of hat cause controversy when she opened Parliament in June 2017, during which she laid out the government's plans for Britain's exit from the European Union?

King Edward VIII, known as the Duke of Windsor after his abdication, is generally credited with having popularized the thick 'full Windsor' knot among tie wearers. However, it was his father, King George V, who is believed to have invented the style.

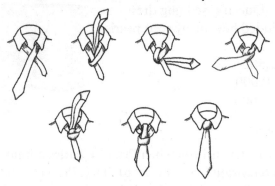

11. Which monarch's clothes-makers had to contend with the unlikely regal vital statistics of a 53-inch chest and a 52-inch waist?

A: Queen Victoria
B: King George III
C: King Henry VIII

12. Which member of the royal family appeared on the cover of British *Vogue's* 100th-anniversary special edition in 2016?

13. The Queen's wedding dress
included how many seed pearls?

A: 1,500
B: 10,000
C: 30,000

14. On the day in 1994 when Prince Charles admitted
in a television interview to adultery, Princess Diana
famously wore a little black dress that was quickly
nicknamed 'the revenge dress'. But who was the
designer responsible for it?

15. G.H. Hurt & Son are the makers of which item of
clothing, supplying examples for Prince Charles, Prince
William, Prince Harry and all of their children too?

16. What colour was the jacket Prince William wore for
his wedding ceremony in 2011?

17. Whom did the Queen sit next to when she unexpectedly arrived to watch Richard Quinn's London fashion show in 2018?

18. What do James Lock & Co. Ltd., Patey (London) Ltd. and Rachel Trevor-Morgan have in common?

19. On which arm do female members of the royal family customarily wear their handbags?

If the Queen moves her handbag to her other arm, her staff understand this as a sign that she wants to finish whatever she is doing (for instance, ending a walkabout). Placing her bag on the table during a dinner is similarly understood as indicating that she wants to leave imminently.

20. Which photographer, originally known for his fashion work, took an iconic series of portraits of Princess Diana in 1997 and subsequently photographed many other royals?

THE ART OF MONARCHY: ROYALTY AND CULTURE

Successful monarchy is always in part about the presentation. Strong rulers and great artists have gone hand-in-hand across the ages. Here's a quiz all about the royal family and their cultural artefacts.

Answers, pages 154–55

1. In 2012 the Royal Collection acquired four screen prints of the Queen by which celebrated American artist of the 20th century?

2. Following Princess Diana's death in 1997, Elton John reworked his hit 'Candle in the Wind' in her honour. But for whom was the song originally written?

3. Which keen royal birdwatcher published a book entitled *Birds from Britannia* in 1962?

4. In 1637, Charles I bought a painting called *The Calling of Saints Peter and Andrew*. For much of its life it has been considered a copy of little financial worth, but in 2006 it was declared an original by one of the great masters, with a value close to £50 million. Who was the artist?

A: Rembrandt van Rijn
B: Caravaggio
C: Sir Anthony Van Dyck

5. Which Oscar-winning designer took official photographic portraits of the Queen on her coronation day?

6. What is the title of Sue Townsend's 1992 novel in which the Queen begins a new life on a council estate after the monarchy is abolished?

7. In 2002, a music concert was staged in the garden of Buckingham Palace to mark the Queen's Golden Jubilee. It included a notable rendition of 'God Save The Queen' by which performer, located on the Palace roof?

8. At the opening of an exhibition of which artist's nudes did the Queen tell one of her aides that she must avoid being 'photographed between a pair of those great thighs'?

9. Since the 17th century, the monarch has appointed a Poet Laureate, an honorary position as poet to the royal court and the nation at large. The role comes with a small salary and a barrel of which consumable?

10. In 2009, which poet became the first woman to hold the post?

Shakespeare's contemporary, Ben Jonson, is often considered the first unofficial Poet Laureate after King James I granted him a pension in the early 17th century. However, John Dryden was the first official incumbent, appointed by Charles II in 1668. But as a Catholic, he refused to pledge allegiance to William and Mary when they ascended the throne a year later, so becoming the only Poet Laureate to be removed from office.

11. Which member of the royal family is a director of Hauser & Wirth art gallery?

A: Sophie, Countess of Wessex
B: Princess Eugenie
C: Lord Freddie Windsor

12. Which legendary jazz musician composed 'The Queen's Suite' for Elizabeth II after meeting her in 1958?

13. In 2008, which Scottish painter contributed a portrait of Zara Phillips to the Sport Relief charity, which sold at auction for £36,000?

14. Which musical instrument did Prince Charles play with the Trinity College orchestra during his time studying at the University of Cambridge?

15. A portrait of Anne of Cleeves has been claimed to have angered Henry VIII for making her appear more beautiful than she was. Who was the artist?

16. Which composer wrote the coronation anthems 'Zadok the Priest', 'Let Thy Hand Be Strengthened', 'The King Shall Rejoice' and 'My Heart Is Inditing'?

17. Judith Weir holds which post within the Royal Household?

Charles I appointed Nicholas Lanier as the first Master of the King's Musick in 1626. He held the post until it lapsed during Oliver Cromwell's rule, but resumed the post after the Restoration in 1660, continuing up until his death in 1666. Among the most famous of the later office-holders was Edward Elgar, who served in the role from 1924–34.

18. Which art expert who held the position of Surveyor of the Queen's Pictures was publicly exposed as a Soviet spy in 1979?

19. Which legendary punk band released their version of 'God Save the Queen' on the day of the Queen's Silver Jubilee in 1977?

20. Of which composer did Queen Victoria write that he was the 'greatest musical genius since Mozart'?

CALL THAT A CURTSY? ROYAL PROTOCOL

Being part of the royal family comes with a lot of rules and traditions, many of which are mystifying to the outsider (and probably to lots of insiders, too). But in the end, mysterious protocol only adds to the institution's allure.

Answers, pages 156–57

1. On which day do the Windsors traditionally open their Christmas presents?

   A: Christmas Eve
   B: Christmas Day
   C: Boxing Day

2. Who was accused of breaking royal protocol when they patted the Queen on the back during a 2019 state visit?

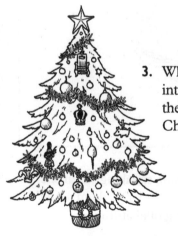

3. Who is considered to have first introduced the royal family to the tradition of putting up a Christmas tree?

4. Where is the Queen's preferred residence for celebrating Easter?

5. On being introduced to the Queen, what is the recommended term of greeting?

According to the official royal website, 'there are no obligatory codes of behaviour' when meeting the Queen. There is certainly no need for bowing and scraping, 'just courtesy'. It suggests a simple neck bow (from the head only) for men, and a small curtsy for women. However, a simple shaking of hands is also acceptable.

6. About whom was Princess Diana speaking when she said, 'You can shake their hands and give them a hug' – words that helped to change global attitudes?

7. In what year was legislation enacted allowing members of the royal family legally to marry Roman Catholics?

8. Prince Philip broke with royal tradition to be present at the birth of all four of his children. True or false?

9. The royal family come together to watch the Queen's speech when it is broadcast on Christmas Day. True or false?

10. Who was the first heir apparent to be born in a hospital, rather than at home as had been tradition?

11. What parliamentary act proclaimed by the Queen in 2019 on the advice of British Prime Minister Boris Johnson, was ruled unlawful by the Supreme Court?

12. What is the name of the financial gift distributed by the Queen each year on the Thursday before Easter Sunday?

13. Each Christmas, the Queen gives which culinary delicacy to about 1,500 of her staff?

14. Since Queen Victoria's wedding in 1840, it has been customary for royal brides to carry a bouquet containing a sprig of which plant that is said to symbolize hope and love?

15. The Queen does not require license plates on her vehicles. True or false?

16. Who said of meeting the Queen: 'I had all this protocol buzzing in my head, and I was like 'don't trip down the stairs and don't touch anybody, whatever you do'? The Queen apparently told them: 'Oh it's all rubbish.'

A: Ronald Reagan
B: Meghan Markle
C: Michelle Obama

17. Princess Diana broke tradition by choosing a ready-made engagement ring available to purchase from a catalogue. True or false?

Prince William proposed to the Duchess of Cambridge using his mother's engagement ring. After Diana died, her two sons each chose a momento to remember her. It was actually Harry who selected the ring, while William went for a watch. However, when William decided the time had come to propose, Harry agreed to a swap. William later explained that passing the ring on to Kate was his way of ensuring his mother did not miss out on his wedding day.

18. The Queen is also the Duke of Lancaster. True or false?

19. How many rounds are fired in a basic royal gun salute?

20. When addressing the Queen as 'Ma'am', ought it to be pronounced to rhyme with 'jam' or 'charm'?

BEHIND
THE SCENES

As the quizzes in the first section were concerned with the public face of the monarchy, the questions in this section are rather more interested in what goes on behind the scenes. The monarchy is very much like the fabled swan, appearing to the onlooker to be gliding gracefully along, while out of sight, under the water, there is an awful lot of furious paddling going on. For the royal family to function, a whole army of individuals is required, making sure that the clan's star turns are fed, watered and navigated safely from A to B each day. Here you will find quizzes on eating and drinking the royal way, royal transportation through the ages, travels both domestic and foreign, as well as a quiz on the theme of royalty on the stage and screen (mediums that have provided valuable insights into what it must be like to be part of the institution in public and in private).

A MEAL FIT FOR A KING: WHAT THE ROYALS EAT AND DRINK

What's the point of being royal if you can't have the best food and drink whenever you so desire it? In fact, many of the modern royals are known for their restraint when it comes to mealtime, but that does not diminish our fascination with how members of the nation's most illustrious family fuel themselves.

Answers, pages 158–59

1. A glass of what cocktail is the Queen said to have before lunch each day?

2. Why did Fiona Cairns shoot to fame in 2011?

3. The Banqueting House is the last remaining part of which Central London palace destroyed by fire in 1698?

4. As of 2019, how many companies held the Queen's royal warrant as purveyors of champagne?

   A: 2
   B: 5
   C: 7

5. What did Queen Victoria like to mix with whisky to make her favourite tipple?

   A: water
   B: ginger ale
   C: claret

6. Prince Charles often starts the day with a boiled egg. For how long does he like it boiled?

7. Which company supplies the Queen with her chocolate mints?

8. Henry VIII attempted to impress the king of France by serving him a cockentrice at a banquet at the Camp du Drap d'Or (Field of the Cloth of Gold) in 1520. But what is a cockentrice?

Henry VIII is known as one of the most gluttonous of monarchs. We know that his waist measurement expanded from 32 inches in 1512 to 54 inches by 1547. However, the most obese monarch of them all was George IV. Unable to curb his appetites in virtually any direction, he eventually grew so fat that he was unable to climb stairs and was thus forced to live and sleep on the ground floor at all times.

9. When the Queen travels, she takes a supply of what sort of tea with her?

10. By what nickname are the Yeomen Warders of Her Majesty's Royal Palace and Fortress the Tower of London often known?

11. Which British monarch gave his name to a popular tuber?

12. The Girl Guides of Australia once gifted the Queen some sugar. Why?

13. What were Harry and Meghan cooking when the prince proposed marriage?

14. In 2018, Prince Charles revealed he regularly skips which meal of the day?

15. The Queen is partial to jam pennies, but what exactly are they?

16. What did the Duchess of Cambridge gift to the Queen during her first Christmas spent with the royal family?

17. The Royal Lochnagar distillery produces a single malt whisky bottled exclusively for which royal estate?

18. How many items of crockery comprise George IV's Grand Service used at state banquets?

A: 800
B: 2,000
C: 4,000

George IV's Grand Service is a lavish silver-gilt affair encompassing everything from egg cups to candelabras. Created by the royal goldsmiths, Rundell, Bridge & Rundell, the initial consignment cost a whopping £60,000 all the way back in 1811 (equivalent to more than £2.5 million in modern money) It was first used at a grand dinner that year, which included a table-top stream running down the middle of the banqueting table, complete with real fish swimming in it. George always knew how to wow his guests!

19. What is the name of the organic food brand established by Prince Charles in 1990?

20. Constance Spry, best known as a florist, is usually credited with creating which dish to celebrate the Queen's coronation?

PLANES, TRAINS AND CARRIAGES: ROYAL TRANSPORT

There can be few such well-travelled individuals
in the world as the Queen and the senior members
of the royal family. So, it's only fair enough that
they get to travel in style. Test your knowledge
of the various ways in which they get around.

Answers, pages 160–61

1. What was the name of the royal barge built to commemorate the Queen's Diamond Jubilee in 2012?

2. The Queen has a mascot that sits upon the bonnet of her royal cars. What is it?

3. Prince Philip qualified to pilot what sort of vehicle in 1956?

4. Although we associate the royals with carriages, they actually only own seven. True or false?

5. What is the name of the coach in which royal brides traditionally travel to their weddings?

6. Which famous means of royal transportation was decommissioned in December 1997?

7. Who was the first monarch to travel by train?

The coach regularly used to transport the Queen to the State Opening of Parliament is known as the Irish State Coach. It was built in 1851 by John Hutton & Sons of Dublin, and exhibited at that city's Great Industrial Exhibition two years later. It was spotted by Queen Victoria on a visit to the exhibition and, taken by its blue, black and gold exterior and damask interior, she bought it for the Royal Collection.

8. On receiving his MBE, triple-World Superbike champion Jonathan Rea revealed which royal had put their own well-known love of motorbike-riding 'on the backburner'?

9. In 2008, Prince Charles converted the Aston Martin he received from his mother for his 21st birthday to run on recycled cooking oil. True or false?

10. On the occasion of her Golden Jubilee in 2002, the Queen received a gift of two new state limousines from which car manufacturer?

11. What are the 'Queen's Messenger' and the 'Royal Sovereign'?

12. Between March 2015 and July 2017 Prince William piloted what sort of vehicles in East Anglia?

13. Which royal walked away unscathed after their BMW was involved in a collision with a bus and a coach at Hyde Park Corner in 2010?

14. Who was the first monarch to travel in a motorcar?

15. The Gold State Coach was used in a coronation for the first time for which monarch?

16. Who was the first member of the royal family to fly in an aeroplane?

17. In 1977, Rolls-Royce designed a bespoke car for the Queen's Silver Jubilee. Upon which of its famous models was it based?

A: Silver Ghost
B: Phantom
C: Silver Shadow

The Gold State Coach, built by the Samuel Butler workshop in London, measures a truly regal 7m (22ft) in length and 3.6m (11.8ft) in height and weighs in at close to 4 tonnes. It cost around £7,000 when it was built, which equates to close to £2 million today. Sir Joseph Wilton contributed elaborate carvings that include cherubs, crowns, palm trees, lions' heads, tritons and dolphins. Yet the Queen's overriding memory of travelling in the coach is that it's 'not very comfortable'!

18. The Queen is a trained mechanic. True or false?

19. The Coventry Transport Museum counts among its collection an unassuming 1980 Austin Mini Metro, but to whom did it belong?

20. On 2 November 1977, the Queen took her first trip on board which iconic aircraft, flying from Barbados to London Heathrow Airport?

A FUNNY THING HAPPENED ON THE WAY TO VANUATU: ROYAL TRAVELS

The Queen has visited well over a hundred countries around the world since her coronation, including every nation within the Commonwealth. That sort of mileage is bound to ensure a bountiful supply of extraordinary traveller's tales, but how much can you recall about royal travels?

Answers, pages 162–63

1. The Queen and Prince Philip are the only British citizens who do not require a passport to travel abroad. True or false.

2. Which foreign country has the Queen visited most often?

3. Elizabeth II became the first British monarch to visit which country in 1986?

4. To which country did the Duke and Duchess of Sussex initially relocate after stepping back from their royal duties in 2020?

5. Where does the royal family customarily spend Christmas and New Year?

6. Which monarch spent just six months of their ten-year reign actually present in England?

7. Where did the Duke and Duchess of Sussex undertake an official tour shortly before announcing their decision to step back from the royal family?

8. The Queen and Prince Philip spent the early part of their honeymoon at which Hampshire property owned by Lord Mountbatten?

9. What is the name of Richard Branson's private Caribbean get-away, which has hosted several royals over the years?

10. During Easter of 1993, newspapers were full of pictures of Princess Diana riding a log flume with her young sons, William and Harry. Where was the log flume?

11. What type of sweet does the Queen consider her trusted cure for jet lag?

12. Outside what famous tourist attraction was Princess Diana notoriously pictured sitting alone in 1992 amid rumours of her collapsing marriage?

13. Who was the first royal to make an official trip to the state of Israel?

14. The Queen reputedly travels with her own supply of sausages, but from which well-known retailer?

15. In 1541, Henry VIII embarked on his Great Progress that saw him ultimately travel from London to which city?

16. The Duke and Duchess of Cambridge spent their honeymoon on the exclusive, private North Island, but to which country does it belong?

17. Princess Margaret regularly holidayed on which island, where she had been gifted a plot of land by Lord Glenconner in 1960?

18. The Queen's luggage is customarily tagged with tabs of which colour?

A: yellow
B: purple
C: red

There are not many countries in the world that have not received an official visit from the Queen at one time or another, but there are a few notable exceptions. She has not visited Greece since taking the throne for instance, which is probably a reflection of the country's fraught history with her husband's family. Similarly, long-standing political sensitivities have effectively ruled out visits to Cuba and to Argentina.

19. In which country was Elizabeth when she was informed of the death of her father (and thus her ascendancy to the throne) in 1952?

20. In 2011 the Queen and Prince Philip visited which country on a state visit, which was the first time a British monarch had visited in a century?

THE PLAY'S THE THING: ROYALTY ON STAGE AND SCREEN

The royal family has been the inspiration for countless portrayals on stage and screen, and the royals have themselves occasionally dabbled in the performing arts. Will your performance on this quiz be worthy of a royal standing ovation?

Answers, pages 164–65

1. In 2000 Prince Charles made a cameo appearance in a 40th-anniversary special of which soap opera?

2. Which actress won an Oscar for her portrayal of the Queen in the 2006 Stephen Frears' film, *The Queen*?

3. Which royal pair have raced against each other in the popular motoring show, *Top Gear*?

   A: Prince Andrew and Sarah Ferguson
   B: Princesses Beatrice and Eugenie
   C: Zara and Mike Tindall

4. Who wrote a one-act play in 1988 entitled *A Question of Attribution*, concerning the secret life of the Queen's chief art adviser?

5. And in the lauded 1991 screen adaptation of *A Question of Attribution*, who played the Queen?

6. What was the name of the legal drama in which Meghan Markle starred as Rachel Zane?

Prior to marrying into the royal family, the Duchess of Sussex was undoubtedly best known for the role of Rachel Zane between 2011 and 2018. But her screen acting CV began almost a decade earlier, with a small role in 2002 in the long-running US soap opera, *General Hospital*. There have been films, too, including box-office hits such as *Get Him to the Greek* and *Horrible Bosses*. In 2020, she received her first film credit as 'Meghan, The Duchess of Sussex' as narrator of a Disney documentary called *Elephant*.

7. Princess Diana danced a duet with whom on the stage of the Royal Opera House in December 1985?

8. Princess Beatrice appeared in the feature film *The Young Victoria*, about the early life of Queen Victoria. True or false?

9. What was the name of Peter Morgan's hit 2013 play, a dramatization of the Queen's weekly meetings with her prime minister?

A: *The Audience*
B: *Secrets and Lies*
C: *Teatime with Her Majesty*

10. William Shakespeare belonged to the acting company known as the King's Men during the reign of James I, but how was the company previously known when Elizabeth I was on the throne?

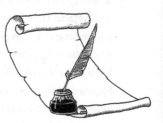

11. In 1971, Prince Charles was filmed giving his impressive impersonation of which beloved *Goon Show* character?

12. Cate Blanchett has starred in a duo of Shekhar Kapur directed films as which monarch?

13. What was the name of the production company formed by Prince Edward in 1993?

14. In 1985, Alan Jay Lerner, the lyricist of *My Fair Lady*, produced an official lullaby called 'Brocades and Coronets'. Who was it for?

15. In which of Shakespeare's plays is England described as 'This royal throne of kings, this scepter'd isle, This earth of majesty'?

Shakespeare wrote 10 acknowledged plays about the kings of England that have deeply coloured our impressions of the monarchs, covering the Plantagenet and Tudor periods: *King John, Richard II, Henry IV (Parts 1 & 2), Henry V, Henry VI (Parts 1, 2 & 3), Richard III* and *Henry VIII*. However, in more recent years it has become widely accepted that he also had a hand in another 'king play', one not published in the famous First Folio of his works –1596's *Edward III*. That play was published anonymously but recent scholarship suggests Shakespeare co-wrote it, possibly with Thomas Kyd or Christopher Marlowe.

16. Which royal appeared in the long-running radio drama, *The Archers*, in 2011, in their real-life role as president of the National Osteoporosis Society?

17. Who was the titular subject of the 2010 Oscar-winning movie, *The King's Speech*?

18. Claire Foy and Olivia Colman both starred as the Queen in which hit Netflix television series?

19. Which irreverent royals-based British sitcom that debuted in 2016 features Harry Enfield and Haydn Gwynne as Charles and Camilla, Hugh Skinner and Louise Ford as William and Kate and Morgana Robinson as Pippa?

20. Judi Dench won an Oscar for an eight-minute portrayal of Elizabeth I in which film?

JUST LIKE THE REST OF US

The quizzes in this section serve as a reminder that while the royals may exist in a world very different from the one most of us inhabit, they are ultimately just humans like you and me. It is often the case that what the majority of us regard as the mundane minutiae of everyday life is held as cherished and exotic in royal circles, where normality is a rare luxury. Moreover, the dynamics of the world's most famous family are perhaps not so different from those of your own, or the family next door. So, let's first explore some of the simple pleasures that many of us share with Her Majesty and the rest of the gang – a love of the animal world and a love of sports. Then it's time to look at royal familial relationships over the years – and you may be surprised by some of those who can claim a connection! There is also a quiz on the subject of royal quirks. Which family doesn't have its eccentricities? The Windsors and their antecedents certainly do and did. Finally, some posers on the great equalizer – death!

NOT ON
THE CARPET!
ROYAL PETS

Over the centuries, the royals have maintained a
close affinity with their animals – from heroic horses
to pampered pooches and much else in between.

Answers, pages 166–67

1. The Queen's dogs are each fed an individually tailored menu. True or false?

2. Who did Edward VII commission in 1907 to make hardstone models of some of his favourite animals?

   A: Charles Rennie Mackintosh
   B: Carl Fabergé
   C: Henri Matisse

3. Which royal issued a statement in 2017 announcing the death of a horse called Toytown, whom they described as 'a huge part of my family, an amazing animal, and a true champion'?

4. The Duke and Duchess of Cambridge own a dog called Lupo, bred from a bitch owned by the duchess's parents in 2011. But what breed is Lupo?

   A: a Dalmatian
   B: an old English sheepdog
   C: an English cocker spaniel

5. To commemorate her 70th birthday in 2015, Princess Michael of Kent was photographed with her beloved pet, Cali. What sort of animal is Cali?

A: a horse
B: a cat
C: a snake

6. George III was the proud owner of 'Miss Jenny' but what was she?

A: a cheetah
B: a tiger
C: a lion

7. Skippy was the first dog to be adopted into the royal family from which famous dog rescue centre, which has been under royal patronage since 1885?

The animal mentioned in question 6 was brought to England in 1764, when it was taken to Windsor Great Park to demonstrate its hunting skills against a stag. Unfortunately, it came off rather worse against the stag's antlers and promptly escaped but was eventually re-caught. George III later commissioned a portrait of 'Miss Jenny', in which she was depicted wearing a red bonnet.

8. The Duchess of Sussex's rescue dog, Guy, shared a car with the Queen before his owner's wedding to Prince Harry. True or false?

9. A dog named Dash received the following elaborate epitaph upon his death:

> '*His attachment was without selfishness,*
> *His playfulness without malice,*
> *His fidelity without deceit,*
> *READER, if you would live beloved and die regretted,*
> *profit by the example of DASH*'.

Who was his regal owner?

10. Which of Henry VIII's six wives was famously depicted by court painter Lucas Horenboult alongside her pet monkey?

11. Which monarch gave his name to a breed of small dog?

12. The Queen was presented with a pair of what by Liberia's President Tubman in 1962?

A: pygmy hippos
B: aardvarks
C: tarantulas

13. In 1956, Princess Anne was gifted which suitably symbolic creature (named Nikki) by Soviet leader, Nikita Khrushchev?

14. Charles I went to the executioner's block accompanied by his favourite dog. True or false?

15. In 1961 on a visit to Gambia, the Queen was presented with a pet that her private secretary apparently kept in his bath until it could be rehoused in a zoo. What kind of animal was it?

16. Which member of the royal family received a criminal record under the Dangerous Dog's Act after their terrier Dotty attacked two children?

In 1235, the Holy Roman Emperor Frederick II gifted Henry III three 'leopards' (in reality, probably lions) that served as the basis of a royal menagerie kept at the Tower of London until the 19th century. In the 13th century, Edward I built a permanent new building for his collection there, in a building that came to be called the Lion Tower.

17. In 1255, the king of France sent what exotic creature to the royal menagerie at the Tower of London, prompting one contemporary observer to note the crowds of Londoners who swarmed 'to see the novel sight'?

A: an African elephant
B: a rhinoceros
C: a vulture

18. In 1252, Henry III received a gift for the royal menagerie believed to have come from the king of Norway. The creature was chained up in the tower but with a 'stout cord' that allowed it to hunt for fish in the River Thames. What was it?

A: an eagle
B: a polar bear
C: a wolf

19. In what pet-related manner did the Queen receive a wound to her hand that required stitches in 1991?

20. As young girls, Princesses Elizabeth and Margaret were the owners of a chameleon. True or false?

A DAY AT THE
RACES: THE ROYALS
AND SPORT

The royals not only attend more sporting events
than most of us could ever dream of (and usually
get to hand out the trophies to boot), but they have a
rich history of being rather good at sport themselves.
Can you get to the top of the quiz podium?

Answers, pages 168–69

1. At what type of sporting event did Prince Charles meet his future wife, Camilla Parker Bowles, in 1971?

2. Elizabeth II received a racehorse called Astrakhan as a wedding gift. Who gave it to her?

   A: her mother
   B: the Aga Khan
   C: the government of Australia

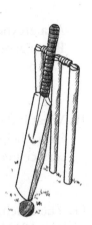

3. Prince Philip has twice been the president of which famous cricket club (in 1949–50 and 1974–75)?

4. What are the Queen's racing colours?

5. Which football team does Prince William support?

6. Prince Harry claimed victory over which sporting legend over a short sprint on his tour of the Caribbean in 2012?

7. The Queen named one of her racehorse's after the two famous footballing brothers, Gary and Phil Neville. True or false?

8. What accolade did Princess Anne receive in 1971 that her daughter, Zara, then won in 2006?

9. As well as horses, the Queen has an extensive collection of another type of racing animal. Arguably the most famous of them was called Sandringham Lightning. But what sort of creature was it?

A: a greyhound
B: a pigeon
C: a pig

10. What is the name of the international games that Prince Harry helped establish for wounded, injured and sick service personnel?

11. The Duchess of Cambridge is the royal patron of The 1851 Trust, which aims to inspire participation in which sport?

A: rowing
B: hockey
C: sailing

12. Which member of the royal family won gold in three-day eventing at the 1972 Munich Olympics, and silver in the same event at the Seoul Olympics 16 years later?

The Duchess of Cambridge is an accomplished sportswoman. She was captain of her school hockey team, is a skilled sailor and a talented rower who, in 2007, was all set to take part in a cross-channel rowing challenge until forced to withdraw because of security concerns.

13. At the 1976 Olympic Games in Montreal, Princess Anne competed for the UK equestrian team. Which normally mandatory testing was she not required to undertake?

A: sex testing
B: drug testing
C: horse examination

14. In 1953, the Queen attended her first football match as monarch – the FA Cup Final between Blackpool and Bolton Wanderers. The match was nicknamed after its star performer, later knighted by the Queen, but who was he?

15. Which rugby union World Cup-winner did Zara Phillips marry?

16. In 1956 the Queen Mother's horse famously led the Grand National by several lengths in the final straight when it inexplicably fell and was overtaken. What was the horse called?

17. Which Swiss ski resort is reputedly Prince Charles's favourite – so much so, that two of the resort's cable cars are named in his honour?

18. Which competitive sport did Prince Philip publish a book about in 1982?

A: clay-pigeon shooting
B: bowls
C: carriage driving

In 1956 Prince Philip instituted the Duke of Edinburgh Awards scheme, one of the aims of which is to encourage young people to keep active and get outdoors. The first director of the scheme was John Hunt, who had successfully led the first expedition to scale Mount Everest.

19. At the 2019 Wimbledon Tennis Championships, the Duchess of Cambridge reportedly revealed that Prince George had received playing tips from which tennis legend and family friend?

20. As part of the London 2012 Olympic Games opening ceremony, the 'Queen' was shown making her entrance into the Olympic Stadium using what dramatic form of transport?

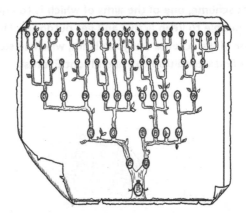

A FAMILY AFFAIR: ROYAL FAMILY CONNECTIONS

The royal family may be an exclusive club,
but its tendrils stretch far and wide. Here's a quiz
exploring some of those familial relationships.

Answers, pages 170–71

1. Judith Keppel was the first person to win the jackpot on the British version of the quiz show *Who Wants to be a Millionaire*? But which member of the royal family is a distant cousin?

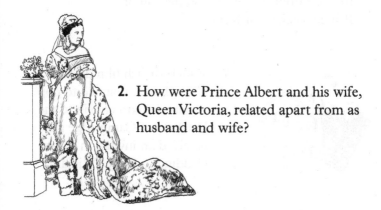

2. How were Prince Albert and his wife, Queen Victoria, related apart from as husband and wife?

3. Which American president was an 11th cousin twice removed to Princess Diana?

4. Who was the Queen and Prince Philip's first grandchild?

5. How many of Henry VIII's children ascended to the throne?

6. Which English actor – whose credits include *CSI: Miami*, *Two and a Half Men* and *Red Dwarf* – is married to Lord Frederick Windsor, the son of Prince Michael of Kent?

7. Which British film director, himself once married to pop royalty, is sixth cousin to the Duchess of Cambridge and received an invitation to her wedding to Prince William?

8. What is the first name of Princess Diana's brother, who famously gave a moving eulogy at her funeral?

9. There has been an enduring theory – comprehensively debunked – that Prince Albert Victor could have been Jack the Ripper. But who was Albert Victor's father?

The Stuarts were one of the great royal dynasties, ruling Scotland from 1371, and then Great Britain and Ireland between 1603 and 1702. While it is commonly believed that the family line died out entirely in 1807, there are nonetheless several individuals around the world today who claim descendancy. Duke Francis of Bavaria certainly has a good claim via marital lines, but another of the more intriguing claimants is a Polish art historian, Peter Pininski, who in 2002 published a well-received book laying out his claim. Fortunately for the Queen, he does not appear to have his sights set on the Crown, however!

10. The Duchess of Cambridge's sister, Pippa, married the brother of which reality TV star?

11. How was Wilhelm II, Emperor of Germany at the outbreak of the First World War, related to Queen Victoria?

12. Who is the first foreign monarch in succession to the British throne?

13. Prince Philip and Prince Charles were father-and-son pupils at which school?

14. What was the name of the estranged wife of King George IV, who turned up to his coronation in 1821 without an invitation and was turned away at the doors of Westminster Abbey?

15. What relation is Prince Edward, Duke of Kent, to the Queen?

16. What surname did Prince Philip adopt when he became a naturalized British subject?

17. What did the Queen call her grandfather, George V, when she was growing up?

A: Grandpa King
B: Grandpa England
C: Grandpa George

18. In 1917, as the First World War raged, George V changed the name of his royal house to Windsor. What had it been immediately before?

> The House of Windsor is the latest in a long line of royal houses that have ruled the United Kingdom, or England and other constituent parts of the kingdom, since William the Conqueror claimed the Crown almost a thousand years ago. George V was the first monarch technically to come from two houses as a result of the name change in question 18. The houses of Normandy, followed by Blois, Anjou, Plantagenet, Lancaster, York, Tudor, Stuart and Hanover came before this.

19. Which twice-Oscar-nominated stage and screen actor – best known as a nemesis of a boy wizard – is an eighth cousin to the Queen's children?

20. Princess Diana's stepmother, Raine, Countess Spencer, was the daughter of which British novelist?

WE ARE A BIT AMUSED: ROYAL QUIRKS

The British royal family is a remarkable institution that inspires admiration and loyalty around the world. Nonetheless, there are some things about it that seem or, indeed, are just a bit odd. Here's a quiz on some of those royal quirks from across the ages.

Answers, pages 172–73

1. The Queen always travels with her own bag of blood.
    True or false?

2. Until 1901, the Royal Household included an official
    whose duties historically involved assisting the monarch
    in going to the toilet. True or false?

3. Royal babies are traditionally christened in holy water
    brought from where?

    A: Canterbury
    B: the River Jordan
    C: Wittenberg

4. The Queen does not like the sound of ice cubes so
    requests drinks are served with 'ice crowns' instead.
    True or false?

5. Henry VIII issued a decree threatening the penalties of
    witchcraft on any woman who 'leads a subject of
    Her Majesty into marriage' by certain specified means
    including the use of 'false hips'. True or false?

6. The Royal Household includes which of the following
    officials?

    A: The Royal Ink Blotter
    B: The Master of the Condiments
    C: The Grand Carver

7. Each year, the Royal Household kidnaps a Member of Parliament. True or false?

> The State Opening of Parliament is full of symbolism, such as the Searching of the Cellars done in recognition of the 17th-century Gunpowder Plot. But perhaps the greatest element of theatre is when the official known as Black Rod goes to the House of Commons to summon members to the House of Lords (where they are not usually permitted) to hear the monarch speak. The Commons' doors are slammed closed in the face of Black Rod as a gesture of the House's independence from the Crown, before Black Rod knocks three times and is then granted admittance to deliver his invitation.

8. In 1969 the royal family made a controversial documentary that attempted to show them as something akin to an 'ordinary' family firm, and which the then controller of BBC Two, David Attenborough, said risked 'killing the monarchy'. True or false?

9. What is a royal peculiar?

    A: a place of worship under the direct control of the
       monarch

    B: an honorific annual payment made to all left-handed
       members of the Royal Household

    C: a sub-breed of corgi with a longer-than-average tail

10. Charles II is believed to have been the first monarch to
decree that six of what type of bird are retained at the
Tower of London at all times?

11. Which monarch insisted that their attendants kiss any
part of the royal bedding that they touched?

12. Which monarch was rumoured to have attempted
to shake hands with a tree, having mistaken it for the
king of Prussia?

13. The Queen would not have been queen had she a
younger brother. True or false?

14. Which monarch attempted to treat their smallpox scars
by regularly applying a face mask containing lead and
arsenic?

15. According to a former royal chef, which of the following foods has the Queen banned from her kitchens?

A: mangoes
B: garlic
C: chocolate

16. Whose physician recommended 'an arthritic powder composed of scrapings of an unburied human skull, herbs, white wine, and whey, to be taken at full moon' as a cure for the monarch's gout?

A: William I
B: James I
C: Charles I

In 1590 James VI of Scotland had been instrumental in establishing the first major witchcraft trials in Scotland, held at North Berwick in East Lothian. His support for the inquiries was influenced by similar trials held in the same year in Denmark, during which black magic was blamed for a series of storms that beset his Danish wife, Anne, on a voyage from her native country to Scotland.

17. In 1597, King James VI of Scotland (later also King James I of England) published a book called *Daemonologie*, a philosophical rumination on black magic and necromancy. Shakespeare is said to have used the book for research related to which of his plays?

18. The Barons Kingsale, holders of what is considered the premier Irish barony, are widely held to enjoy what is called the 'De Courcy privilege'. The privilege allows them to do which of the following?

A: wear a hat in the presence of the monarch
B: turn their back on the monarch
C: kiss the monarch on the lips

19. The Isles of Scilly Wildlife Trust, which manages around 60 per cent of the area of the isles off the coast of Cornwall, pay an annual rent to Prince Charles as the Duke of Cornwall. What do they pay him?

A: a single penny
B: a quart of fresh milk and a pound of honey
C: a single daffodil

20. The monarch may lay claim to any mermaid within three miles of British shores. True or false?

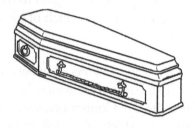

WHAT A WAY TO GO: ROYAL DEATHS

It does not matter how high born you are, death is the great equalizer. In fact, being of royal blood has historically given you a reasonable chance of meeting a particularly unhappy ending. Find out how much you can recall of royal dispatches.

Answers, pages 174–75

1. Who was the last English monarch to die on the battlefield?

2. What significant role did Henri Paul have in the death of Princess Diana?

3. According to legend, which English king died when he was stabbed up the bottom while sitting on his toilet?

4. How many of Henry VIII's wives were executed?

5. Henry I died of food poisoning, but was it caused by rotten venison or too much fish?

6. The Duke of Windsor, previously Edward VIII, died in 1972 at his home in which European city?

7. Which king's last words were reputedly, 'Let not poor Nelly starve'?

   A: Henry VIII
   B: Charles II
   C: George III

8. Queen Victoria was buried with a picture and lock of hair of whom clutched in her left hand?

> Victoria died at Osborne House, her retreat on the Isle of Wight, on 22 January 1901. Victoria was buried wearing a white dress and her wedding veil. Among the items placed in her coffin were one of Prince Albert's dressing gowns and a plaster cast of his hand.

9. Which English king died from dysentery not long after crossing the marshy area in East Anglia known as The Wash, a journey during which he lost a large part of his worldly wealth when it was washed away?

10. Whose corpse was said to have either exploded or leaked from its coffin while at Syon Abbey near London, with the remains licked from the floor by dogs?

11. Which monarch was executed at Fotheringhay Castle in Northamptonshire?

12. The death of George VI was communicated using the code phrase 'Fortnum & Mason'. True or false?

13. Richard III's body was discovered in 2012 buried underneath a car park in which English city?

14. In 1478, George Plantagenet, Duke of Clarence, was killed in the Tower of London, where he was imprisoned for treason against his brother, Edward IV. He was said to have died by drowning, but in what substance?

    A: mead
    B: whisky
    C: Malmsey wine

15. What was the name of the English king reputedly killed by an arrow to the eye at the Battle of Hastings?

16. Whose doctor suggested in his diary that he had administered fatal doses of morphine and cocaine in part so that the monarch's death might be reported in the morning edition of *The Times* and not in 'less appropriate...evening journals'?

17. Whose last words were: 'I go from a corruptible to an incorruptible Crown, where no disturbance can be, no disturbance in the world.'

18. What were the names of the 'princes in the Tower' last seen at the Tower of London in 1483 and widely suspected of having been murdered there?

> Richard III, the princes' uncle and Lord Protector during Edward's brief reign, has long been considered prime suspect in the disappearance of the brothers. However, there is little in the way of firm evidence linking him to their presumed deaths. Bones from two unknown children were discovered at the Tower in 1674, with King Charles II ordering the bones be taken to Westminster Abbey and put in an urn bearing the names of the two princes.

19. Which member of the royal family was killed in 1942 when the military plane he was taking to Iceland crashed in Scotland?

20. Which close relation of the Queen and Prince Philip was killed by an Irish Republican Army bomb on 27 August 1979?

PRIVATE LIVES

Now it's time to get personal! In the quizzes that follow in this section, we will be delving into the private lives of the royals. In recent times, the royal family has had to endure a level of public scrutiny that it is surely unfair to expect anyone to have to bear. Sure enough, under the microscope of an often-ruthless media, their foibles and indiscretions have been regularly exposed. On top of that, they routinely find themselves the subjects of scurrilous rumour, guilty of nothing more than being considered fair game by reporters and editors hungry for a front-page splash. At least in the old days, a royal dandy could expect tales of his ill behaviour to be restricted to a privileged few among the aristocracy! Now it's your turn to dive into a sea of salaciousness, rumour and gossip, encompassing royal love lives, stately scandal, tabloid tittle-tattle and some startling celebrity connections.

SNOG, MARRY, AVOID: ROYAL LOVE LIVES

Being royal brings extra complications to your personal life – lack of privacy, muck-raking journalists and disparate opinions on who qualifies as a suitable love interest are just a few of the impediments to a normal, happy private life. But, goodness, it does make for some interesting stories!

Answers, pages 176–77

1. Which TV presenter, who rose to fame as a weather reporter on morning television, has claimed she once briefly dated Prince Edward?

2. What was the profession of Antony Armstrong-Jones at the time of his marriage to Princess Margaret in 1960?

3. Which royal's planned May 2020 wedding at the Chapel Royal at St James's Palace was postponed as a result of the Covid-19 pandemic?

4. While prince regent, George IV secretly married in an illegal ceremony in London. True or false?

5. Which royal's spouse previously managed the Mayfair nightclub and famous royal haunt, Mahiki?

6. How many times was Wallis Simpson divorced?

The abdication crisis of the 1930s for a while seemed to pose an existential threat to the institution of the monarchy. Edward VIII was determined to wed his already married lover, Wallis Simpson, an intention deemed incompatible with his kingly role as head of the Church of England. Edward's actions split opinion, and the Canadian premier, Mackenzie King, was among those not sorry to see him go. 'If that is the kind of man he is,' he wrote in his diary, 'it is better he should not be longer on the throne.'

7. In 1992, intimate photos were published of the Duchess of York and her financial advisor while she was holidaying in Saint-Tropez. What was his name?

8. Which member of the pop band The Saturdays dated Prince Harry briefly in 2012?

9. Which former husband of a member of the royal family rode as an amateur in the 1969 Grand National?

10. Which royal couple – parents to two children – announced their intention to divorce in February 2020?

11. In 1992, a transcript was published in the media, of a telephone conversation between Princess Diana (who was still married to Prince Charles at the time) and a man named James Gilbey. By what now notorious nickname did he refer to the princess over 50 times in the call?

12. What is the name of Princess Anne's second husband, whom she married in 1992?

13. What was the name of the woman, a widowed mother of two, whom Edward IV married for love against the advice of most of his advisors?

14. From 1982 until 1983, Prince Andrew dated which American actress, whose credits included a starring role in the 1976 movie, *Emily*?

15. How did a New Zealand art teacher called Heather Tonkin find herself the subject of international headlines in 1991?

A: She was reported to be dating Prince Edward.
B: Princess Anne's then husband, Captain Mark Phillips, was revealed as the father of her seven-year-old child.
C: Old school-friend Princess Diana had been writing to her about her marriage problems.

16. Before marrying Anne Boleyn, Henry VIII had an affair with her sister. What was her name?

17. The British-American actress and 'It Girl', Lillie Langtry, was a lover of which future king?

Jersey-born Lillie Langtry seemed almost destined to fill the gossip columns of Victorian Britain. Blessed with beauty and social graces, she became a fixture in the most glamorous social scenes on both sides of the Atlantic. Nor was the king mentioned in question 17 her only high-born lover. She also famously had relationships with the Earl of Shrewsbury and Prince Louis of Battenberg, the father of Lord Louis Mountbatten of Burma.

18. What was the name of the divorced royal equerry whom Princess Margaret intended to marry before the couple split in 1955?

19. During her wedding vows, Princes Diana stumbled over Prince Charles's name. What new first name did she briefly give him?

A: Philip
B: George
C: Andrew

20. Prince Harry took Meghan Markle on a night-time date to the Natural History Museum in London. True or false?

ANNUS HORRIBILIS: ROYAL SCANDAL AND STRIFE

The Queen herself once noted: 'Like all the best families, we have our share of eccentricities, of impetuous and wayward youngsters and of family disagreements'. Here is a quiz to give a flavour of the problems and trials they have faced.

Answers, pages 178–79

1. Which year did the Queen famously refer to as her 'annus horribilis' in her Christmas address?

2. Guy Fawkes famously tried to blow up the House of Lords in 1605, but which monarch was the target of his plot?

3. In 2010, Sarah, Duchess of York, was filmed apparently offering access to her ex-husband, Prince Andrew, for £500,000. The sting operation was conducted by a *News of the World* journalist known by which nickname?

4. Prince Harry was forced to apologize in 2005 after he was pictured wearing what to a fancy-dress party?

5. What was the name of Mary, Queen of Scot's murdered second husband?

The body of Mary's husband, and that of his valet, were discovered in the orchard of a house near Edinburgh, where he had been recuperating from a bout of ill health. Earlier in the night there had been a large explosion at the house, thought by contemporaries to have caused fatal internal injuries, although others suggested he was strangled. A little less than a year earlier, he had played a part in the brutal murderous stabbing of Mary's private secretary, David Rizzio. Bloody times!

6. The magazine *Closer* was forced to pay damages in 2017 after publishing topless photographs of which member of the royal family?

7. Which of the following acts gained notoriety for a youth called Edward Jones?

A: He knocked down one of the Queen's corgis on his skateboard.
B: He stole Queen Victoria's underwear.
C: He screamed loudly while the youngest guest at Charles and Diana's wedding.

8. Following worldwide interest in a particular part of their anatomy, which royal insider later reflected: 'As I found out, recognition has its upside, its downside and – you may say – its backside'.

9. In 2001, Prince Edward found himself embroiled in a scandal when his own television production company was accused of invading the privacy of which royal?

10. George V and Queen Mary's sixth son, John, spent several years hidden away from public view on the Sandringham estate before dying at the age of 13. From which condition did he suffer?

11. Controversy over his friendship with which convicted offender led Prince Andrew to step back from his royal duties in 2019?

12. Shortly before her wedding to Prince Edward in 1999, a topless photo of Sophie Rhys-Jones (as she then was) taken in 1988 was published in the British press. Who was the famous broadcaster who featured in the photo alongside her?

13. In 1963, the papers sated the hunger for royal gossip by reporting that the then 14-year-old Prince of Wales had bought alcohol in a public bar while on a school trip. But what was his tipple of choice?

A: a pint of IPA bitter
B: a bottle of champagne
C: a measure of cherry brandy

14. How did Sarah Forsyth come to play an important role in Prince Harry's life?

    A: She represented him in a legal action against an American newspaper.

    B: She was one of his teachers at Eton, where she claimed she was told to ghostwrite a project for him.

    C: She was his fellow guest at a notorious Las Vegas party and leaked photos of the event.

15. Who was the monarch at the time of the Great Fire of London?

16. Photos of Princess Margaret and which of her lovers holidaying in Mustique caused a scandal when they were published in the press in 1976?

> Margaret reputedly considered Mustique as 'the only place I can relax', and she usually visited at least twice a year, hosting parties that became quite legendary. Her friendship with another sometimes-Mustique resident, Rolling Stone Mick Jagger in particular fuelled tabloid speculation for many years.

17. Who was the intended victim of a failed kidnapping attempt on The Mall in London in 1974?

18. Which royal form of address did Princess Diana lose as a result of her divorce to Prince Charles?

19. In 2019, Meghan, Duchess of Sussex, began legal action against a Sunday newspaper for what she claimed was its illegal publication of a private letter sent by her to whom?

20. Whose at the time controversial relationship with Queen Victoria was the subject of a 2017 feature film?

A: her Indian attendant, Abdul Karim
B: her Scottish attendant, John Brown
C: her Conservative prime minister, Benjamin Disraeli

TABLOID TITTLE-TATTLE: ROYAL RUMOURS

Even in the age of the Kardashians, the royals are still surely the most talked about family on the planet. But separating the fact from the fiction can be quite a challenge. How good are you at teasing out the truth?

Answers, pages 180–81

1. The Queen used butterfly nets to capture bats until well into old age. True or false?

2. Prince Edward once auditioned for *Britain's Got Talent* using a disguise and a false name but failed to make it through the preliminary round. True or false?

3. Zara Phillips paid £35 to have her tongue pierced as a teenager. True or false?

4. Prince Charles has his shoelaces ironed flat each day. True or false?

5. The Queen forbade Zara Phillips from accepting an invitation to be a permanent team captain on *A Question of Sport*. True or false?

6. Princess Anne always lays a £100 wager on the Grand National and has an 80 per cent success rate in predicting the winner. True or false?

7. Prince William has a 'Harry Potter scar' on his forehead that he received when he was hit with a golf club. True or false?

8. When Prince William was a small boy, he used to call the Queen 'Gary'. True or false?

One unlikely name by which the Queen is sometimes known is 'Brenda'. This is the result of the satirical magazine *Private Eye* bestowing the nickname upon her in 1971. At the time, there had been a recent film in which the royal family attempted to provide an insight into their 'ordinary' family dynamics. Brenda, *Private Eye* decided, was just the sort of 'ordinary' name the Queen might have, and in some quarters it stuck. Rumour has it, though, that Prince Philip's favoured moniker for his wife is 'Cabbage'!

9. Prince Harry has raced against Olympic champion swimmer, Ryan Lochte. True or false?

10. The Queen has a member of staff to 'break in' her hats to make sure the brims don't rub. True or false?

11. Prince Charles has conducted London's celebrated Philharmonia Orchestra. True or false?

12. Prince Charles always travels with his own personal white leather toilet seat. True or false?

13. Prince Philip once took on the world's strongest man, Geoff Capes, in a Shredded Wheat eating contest. True or false?

14. William and Kate received a tandem bike as a wedding gift from the then Mayor of London (and the future prime minister), Boris Johnson. True or false?

15. It is technically a treasonable offence to eat a swan without royal permission in the UK. True or false?

16. Prince Philip is worshipped as a god on one particular Pacific Island. True or false?

Royal relations with the press have often been strained, perhaps never more so than when paparazzi were implicated in the death of Princess Diana. Her son, Harry, has been particularly vocal in his condemnation of certain parts of the media, with he and his wife formally breaking off relations with certain newspapers in early 2020. His grandfather, Prince Philip, had previously described one daily newspaper as 'bloody awful... full of lies, scandal and imagination'. Quite!

17. King George V had a tattoo that read 'Mother' in Japanese script. True or false?

18. The Queen has sat on the Iron Throne from *Game of Thrones*. True or false?

19. Meghan Markle played 'the Banker' in the US version of the game show, *Deal or No Deal*. True or false?

20. In 2011, Princess Anne's son-in-law Mike Tindall was fined and banned from England rugby's elite player squad for taking part in a dwarf-throwing competition during that year's World Cup in New Zealand. True or false?

CELEBRITY FRIENDS: ROYAL CONNECTIONS TO THE RICH AND FAMOUS

Of course, celebrity and royalty have long gone together, but some associations are more intriguing than others. Dive in to explore some of the most notable celeb-to-royal connections!

Answers, pages 182–83

1. On the popular TV genealogy show, *Who Do You Think You Are?*, which actor was revealed to be descended from William I, Henry III and Henry VIII's advisor, Thomas Cromwell?

2. Which singer reportedly suffered a cut face in 2016 when he was struck with a sword by Princess Beatrice during a mock knighting of performer James Blunt?

3. Which Scottish-born actor, known for roles in TV hits including *Downton Abbey*, *Game of Thrones* and *The Good Fight*, is a descendant of Charles II?

4. Which band, who in their heyday were leaders of the New Romantic movement, did Princess Diana regularly cite as her favourite band?

5. Which tragic British TV presenter's burgeoning relationship with Prince Harry was brought to a close in 2009? She would later write, 'To meet a prince is so unlikely, it would be weird not to acknowledge it. However, once the story got out, that was it. We had to stop seeing each other'.

6. Which sportsman and friend of Prince Harry suggested he would throw three stag parties for the prince ahead of his wedding to Meghan Markle, saying 'My idea is to have one in Kingston, one in Vegas, and one in London'?

7. Which British Oscar-winning actor was in Prince William's year at Eton?

Both Prince William and Harry went to Eton, arguably the most famous public school in the kingdom – although they were the first British royals to attend for some years. Among William's close contemporaries at the school were actor Tom Hiddleston and the singer-songwriter, Frank Turner.

8. Which inventor once wrote of Queen Victoria that she was 'humpy, stumpy, dumpy' and that her hands were 'red, coarse, and fat as a washerwoman's and her face also fat and florid'?

A: Alexander Graham Bell
B: Guglielmo Marconi
C: Thomas Edison

9. Which tennis legend has the Duchess of Sussex referred to as among her 'closest friends'?

10. Prince Harry took to the stage with which band at the close of a 2016 concert in Kensington Gardens for the Prince's Sentebale charity?

A: The Killers
B: Coldplay
C: One Direction

11. Stuart Hall, Les Dawson and Su Pollard were hosts of which notorious television production in 1987?

12. Which performer – who rose to fame as a Disney child star – is an 18th cousin of the Queen?

A: Justin Timberlake
B: Hilary Duff
C: Christina Aguilera

13. Which model, socialite and actress – whose credits include a major role in the television drama *White House Farm* – dated Prince Harry between 2012 and 2014?

14. With which famous rock musician did Princess Diana fall out in 1997 over the publication of a book by fashion designer Gianni Versace?

15. Which much-loved television producer and presenter produced the Queen's Christmas speeches between 1986 and 1991?

16. Which singer performed the song that accompanied William and Kate's wedding reception first dance?

As might be expected, the wedding guest list of Prince William and Kate Middleton in 2011 numbered the great and the good from around the world. From the world of celebrity were the likes of comedian Rowan Atkinson, footballing legend Sir Trevor Brooking, rugby World Cup-winning coach Sir Clive Woodward, recording superstar Sir Elton John, singer Joss Stone and photographer Mario Testino. Prince Harry and Meghan Markle were not to be outdone in 2018, counting among their guests James Blunt, George and Amal Clooney, Idris Elba, Oprah Winfrey, Carey Mulligan and Marcus Mumford.

17. Which celebrity power couple were guests at the weddings of both Prince William and Prince Harry, having previously been photographed sitting on thrones at their own 1999 wedding?

18. Which double-Oscar-winning British actress asked Prince William for a kiss when she received a damehood from him in 2018?

19. Which musician caused a commotion at the 1963 Royal Variety Performance when he commented: 'For our last number, I'd like to ask your help. The people in the cheaper seats, clap your hands. And the rest of you, if you'd just rattle your jewellery'.

20. Which pop star caused a furore in 1997 when she reportedly pinched Prince Charles's bottom ahead of a Prince's Trust Concert?

FACTS AND FIGURES

After all that debauchery, it's time to re-establish some decorum. Here's your chance to find out how much you know about the nuts and bolts of royal history. There's a quiz on key dates from throughout the institution's rich past, another to test your knowledge of quotable royals past and present, as well as an examination of some of the most notable royal records and historic firsts. Then, to conclude, a good old-fashioned test of your regal general knowledge. Pass these challenges and so demonstrate your fidelity to the Crown, and you may expect a summons to the palace to be honoured by Her Majesty. Fail, and it will be the fast track to the executioner's block on Tower Hill. And that's a fact! (Or maybe not...)

WHAT ARE YOU TALKING ABOUT? QUOTATIONS BY AND ABOUT THE ROYAL FAMILY

We love to talk about the royals and to forensically analyse their words too. So, how much can you recall about which royal said what, and what has been said about them?

Answers, pages 184–85

1. Which pop princess once said of Prince William: 'We exchanged emails for a little bit, and he was supposed to come and see me, but it didn't work out.'

   A: Britney Spears
   B: Christine Aguilera
   C: Cheryl Cole

2. Which monarch notoriously said: 'Princes are not bound to give an account of their actions but to God alone'?

3. In 1995, Princess Diana said during an interview on the BBC's *Panorama* programme: 'Well, there were three of us in this marriage, so it was a bit crowded.' But who was the interviewer?

4. George VI is said to have once commented of the royal family: 'We are not a family, we are __ _____.' What are the missing words?

   A: an institution
   B: an asylum
   C: a firm

Queen Victoria might have had a reputation for glumness but she was quite the one for bon mots. On the occasion of a failed assassination attempt in 1882, she is quoted as saying: 'It is worth being shot at to see how much one is loved'.

5. Which world figure described the Queen as a 'spectacular woman', adding that they 'had automatic chemistry'?

6. Which member of the royal family said in a speech on International Women's Day in 2015: 'I am proud to be a woman and a feminist'?

7. Which monarch famously told his people: 'You must believe me when I tell you that I have found it impossible to carry the heavy burden of responsibility and to discharge my duties as king as I would wish to do without the help and support of the woman I love.'

8. In 1984, Prince Charles – a noted critic of modern architecture – described the extension to which building as being 'like a monstrous carbuncle on the face of a much-loved and elegant friend'?

9. In a statement made on behalf of the British people in 1969, the Queen said: 'May this endeavour increase the knowledge and wellbeing of mankind'. What was the endeavour?

10. Which member of the royal family once claimed: 'I'm not going to be some person in the royal family who just finds a lame excuse to go abroad and do all sorts of sunny holidays and whatever'?

11. Which monarch is said to have uttered the phrase 'We are not amused', apparently in response to the telling of an inappropriate story during a dinner at Windsor Castle?

12. To which question asked by documentary-maker Tom Bradbury in 2019 did Meghan Markle respond: 'I guess, also thank you for asking, because not many people have asked…'?

13. Who described Prince Charles as a 'little grovelling bastard' after the prince paid tribute to him at the 1994 British Comedy Awards?

14. In a 2019 interview widely regarded as misjudged, Prince Andrew claimed he had been celebrating his daughter's birthday where, at a time when he was alleged to have been in a London nightclub?

15. Who did the Queen describe as having 'an infectious zest for living' that remained with them 'until the very end'?

16. Who is said to have described Henry VIII as a 'pig, dolt and liar'?

A: Anne Boleyn
B: Martin Luther
C: Henry VII

17. According to legend, whose last words – uttered in response to a suggestion that he might visit the seaside resort when fully recovered – were 'Bugger Bognor'?

18. Who said of Princess Diana shortly after her death: 'She was the people's princess and that is how she will stay, how she will remain in our hearts and our memories forever'?

Being a royal can be tough – a role that demands expressive enthusiasm when meeting the public, combined with the ability to bite one's tongue. Some are better at it than others. Prince Philip, for example, is notorious for a series of gaffes where he has 'misspoken' in public. George V's wife, Queen Mary, perhaps put it best when addressing a member of the family who was complaining of being tired and sick of visiting hospitals. 'You are a member of the British royal family,' Mary told them. 'We are never tired, and we all love hospitals.'

19. Which Hollywood star said of dancing with Princess Diana at the White House in 1985: 'Only in storybooks do you get to dance with a princess until midnight. But it happened to me'?

A: Richard Gere
B: John Travolta
C: Robert Redford

20. Of which famous landmark did Elizabeth II say that 'it looks very damp'?

LONG TO
REIGN OVER US:
ROYAL FIRSTS AND
OTHER RECORDS

Elizabeth II became Britain's longest-reigning
monarch in 2015 when she surpassed the 63 years
and 216 days of the previous record holder, Queen
Victoria. Two years later, Elizabeth became the first
to celebrate a Sapphire Jubilee. But how much do
you know about other regal records and firsts?

Answers, pages 186–87

1. Which monarch was the oldest to ascend the throne, at the age of 64 years (or 23,684 days)?

2. Who, in 2010, became the first member of the royal family to complete the London Marathon?

   A: The Duchess of Cambridge
   B: Zara Tindall
   C: Princess Beatrice

3. How many great-grandchildren did Queen Victoria have?

   A: 33
   B: 58
   C: 83

4. Which monarch was the tallest?

5. And who has the record for being the shortest?

6. Who was the first monarch to visit the United States of America?

7. Which monarch was the first to claim sovereignty over England, Scotland and Ireland?

8. Can you name the monarch who had the most legitimate children?

> **The British monarch with the most children overall was Henry I (1068–1135), who could boast a jaw-dropping 20-plus offspring. However, of this total only two (or perhaps three) were legitimate.**

9. How did Henry Collen find himself involved in a notable first involving Queen Victoria in 1844?

   A: Was he the doctor who assisted her as she became the first queen to give birth to twins?
   B: Did he take the first photograph of a British monarch?
   C: Was he the postman who delivered the first letter to the Queen using the Royal Mail?

10. What did Elizabeth I become the first monarch to possess after John Harington installed one in her palace at Richmond?

11. Elizabeth I was also the first monarch recorded as wearing which silk garment after she was gifted a pair by her 'silk woman', Alice Montagu, in 1560?

    A: stockings
    B: knickers
    C: bow tie

12. George V gave the first broadcasted Christmas message, delivered from Sandringham in 1932. Who scripted it?

13. Who were the first royal couple to have their marriage televised?

    A: The Queen and Prince Philip
    B: Princess Margaret and Antony Armstrong-Jones
    C: Prince Charles and Princess Diana

14. Edward VIII was the first British monarch to abdicate. True or false?

15. There have been eight kings named Henry and eight named Edward, but what is the next most popular name for British kings?

16. Who was the first monarch or heir to the throne to complete a university degree course?

17. Who was the first crowned queen of England?

The monarch who can claim the shortest reign was Lady Jane Grey, who was proclaimed monarch in succession to Edward VI on 10 July 1553 but relinquished her claim only nine days later. Although Edward had named her as his successor in his will, in truth her claim to the throne was always shaky and political events soon overtook her. She was imprisoned for treason and executed in 1554.

18. In which year was the Queen's Christmas speech televised in colour for the first time?

A: 1962
B: 1965
C: 1967

19. Who was the first Prince of Wales?

20. Who is the only monarch to have been born and to have died at Buckingham Palace?

1066 AND ALL THAT: FAMOUS DATES IN ROYAL HISTORY

Royalty is so fascinating because of the richness
of its history. How good is your memory?
When did the following royal events –
some ancient, some recent – take place?

Answers, pages 188–89

1. The Queen was born on 21 April 1926 but when is her official birthday traditionally celebrated?

2. Which of the Queen's children was born on 15 August 1950?

3. Which king was crowned on Christmas day?

4. Prince Charles married Camilla Parker Bowles on 9 April in which year?

5. Which accolade did Queen Elizabeth II receive from *TIME* magazine in 1952?

6. William and Kate had their second child in what year?

7. In which decade was Elizabeth I crowned?

8. Queen Elizabeth, the Queen Mother was 101 when she died on 30 March of which year?

9. Which year of the 20th century saw three kings on the British throne?

Before the 20th century, there were two other years in which the English throne bore three monarchs. In 1066, Edward the Confessor died in the January to be succeeded by King Harold, who was then killed at the Battle of Hastings and succeeded by William the Conqueror. There was even time for another claimant, Edgar Ætheling, or Edgar II, who made a claim to the Crown between Harold's death and William's coronation. Then, in 1483, Edward IV died and was succeeded by his son, Edward V, who was usurped by Richard III before the year was out.

10. In which year was the Queen's coronation?

11. George II was the last reigning monarch to lead troops into battle, when he met the French at the Battle of Dettingen. But in which decade did the event occur?

12. In which year did Queen Victoria ascend the throne?

13. Who celebrates their birthday on 14 November?

    A: Prince Charles
    B: Prince Philip
    C: Prince Harry

14. In which year did King John assent to the Magna Carter?

15. In which year did Sarah Ferguson marry Prince Andrew?

16. In which year did Charles I lose his head?

    A: 1642
    B: 1649
    C: 1660

17. Which member of the royal family was born at 8.18 pm on 8 August (the eighth month) in 1988?

18. What year witnessed the Glorious Revolution that saw William of Orange and Mary II replace James II on the throne?

A: 1666
B: 1677
C: 1688

> The Glorious Revolution, a name coined by English parliamentarian John Hampden, was essentially a religious battle between the supporters of the Catholic James II of England and VII of Scotland, and those of his eldest daughter, the Protestant Anne. When James had a son when he was in his 50s, there was the real prospect of a Catholic dynasty. With her Dutch Protestant husband, William of Orange, Anne moved against her father, forcing him into exile before the year's end in a virtually bloodless coup and commencing a co-reign with her husband.

19. What was particularly notable about the Trooping the Colour in 1981?

20. The Great Exhibition was one of the high points in the reign of Queen Victoria but in which year was it held?

A ROYAL
RUMMAGE

To finish off, a potpourri of royal trivia!

Answers, pages 190–91

1. What was the Queen's nickname among her family when young?

   A: Queen Bess
   B: Lilibet
   C: Lizzielops

2. Who walked Meghan Markle down the aisle at her wedding to Prince Harry?

3. Who was the first of the Queen's prime ministers to have been born during her reign?

4. Which monarch once proclaimed that 'I have the heart and stomach of a king, and of a king of England too'?

5. Why is Bruton Street in London of particular note to the royal family?

6. Prince Philip was born a prince of Greece and which other country?

Prince Philip endured a fraught start to his life, which started in Greece in 1921. Within a year of his birth, his uncle, the king, had been forced to abdicate and his father was arrested by the new military government. Forced into exile, Philip and his family were transported in a British naval vessel to begin a new life, initially in France. On that voyage away from his homeland, the tiny Philip was reduced to sleeping in a cot made from an old fruit box!

7. What official duty united Princess Margaret, Princess Alexandra of Kent, Lady Caroline Montagu-Douglas-Scott, Lady Mary Cambridge, Lady Elizabeth Lambert, Pamela Mountbatten, Margaret Elphinstone and Diana Bowes-Lyon?

8. Who designed Meghan Markle's wedding dress?

9. Prince Charles was invested as the Prince of Wales at which Welsh castle in 1969?

10. What surname did Prince William use when he was
a student at St Andrew's University?

11. Under whose rule was an edict issued that prohibited
anyone from appearing at the royal court wearing shirts
with 'outrageous double ruffs' or hose of 'monstrous
and outrageous greatness'?

A: Mary I
B: Elizabeth I
C: Charles I

12. Prince Charles has twice guest edited which
publication?

13. A 1526 inventory of Henry VIII's wardrobe show
he owned what item of sporting apparel?

A: jodhpurs
B: football boots
C: tennis shorts

14. After the death of George VI in 1952, the BBC stopped
airing all comedy until after his funeral. True or false?

15. The Queen's cheque books are emblazoned with a corgi. True or false?

16. The Queen is the only female student to have attended Eton College. True or false?

17. In June 1349, Edward III banned the playing of which sport in order that men might not be distracted from practising archery, which was considered an essential skill for the nation's wellbeing?

18. Of which royal correspondent did Prince Charles say, in a conversation picked up by journalists' microphones: 'These bloody people. I can't bear that man. I mean, he's so awful, he really is'?

19. When she is in residence at Buckingham Palace, Windsor Castle, Holyroodhouse or Balmoral, the Queen can hear what type of musician playing beneath her window each morning?

20. What are the Queen's middle names?

Crowning Glories: Royal Treasures

1. The Tower of London.

2. Sir Edwin Lutyens (1869–1944). His expansive body of work included everything from English country houses to civic buildings in New Delhi, not to mention the Cenotaph in London's Whitehall. If the doll's house was not his most monumental work, it was nonetheless remarkable in its own right. Among its claims to fame, it is the largest construction of its type in the world, and comes complete with electricity, running water and working lifts.

3. A: George Bernard Shaw. The doll's house featured contributions from over 1,500 notable craftsmen and manufacturers. Bernard Shaw was not the only creative to refuse to collaborate: Edward Elgar turned down the request to donate a musical score dismissing the project as 'trivial'. Shaw's exact reasons for declining are uncertain although he is said to have turned down the invitation in a long and offensive letter.

4. C: 23,000.

5. Charles II, in 1661. The crown is named in honour of the sainted 11th-century king, Edward the Confessor. The original of the crown, used in coronations since the 13th century, was sold or melted down during the English Civil War in the 1640s.

6. Carl Fabergé.

7. J.M.W. Turner. Turner took the liberty of amalgamating events from the battle that occurred over several days into a single dramatic scene.

8. Mahatma Gandhi.

9. The Stone of Scone, a large, rectangular block of sandstone associated with the crowning of Scottish monarchs until its removal to England in 1296.

10. The Archbishop of Canterbury.

11. The Koh-i-Noor, meaning 'mountain of light'.

12. False – the jewels were melted down, but the metal was used to mint coins to pay the troops who had defeated the king.

13. B: 5,500.

14. Leonardo da Vinci.

15. C: an elephant called Jumbo – it was in turn gifted by the Queen to London Zoo.

16. True. He took the Prince of Wales Crown that he had worn at his father's coronation in 1911 and it was not returned to the UK until after his death.

17. Colonel Thomas Blood who, along with two accomplices, tricked the Keeper of the Jewel House into allowing them to touch the jewels before attacking him. Since the attempted robbery the jewels have never again been on open display.

18. He became Crown Jeweller.

19. The Cullinan I (also known as the Great Star of Africa). The uncut gem from which this diamond is cut was discovered in 1905 in South Africa and cut to make 105 stones in total.

20. B: Postman Pat. Charles was visiting a studio that had been involved in creating an animated movie of the popular postal worker.

One's Home is One's Castle: Royal Homes

1. Thomas Wolsey. With his star fading in the royal court, Wolsey gave the palace at Richmond-upon-Thames (southwest of London) to Henry VIII in 1529 in a bid to curry favour. Wolsey had commenced building the palace some 14 years earlier.

2. True. The king was persuaded into the move by the prime minister, David Lloyd George. However, the king is thought to have been rather annoyed to be denied his wine.

3. Hillsborough Castle. Located in County Down, Hillsborough Castle is the official home of the Secretary of State for Northern Ireland and a royal residence. In 1998 negotiations for the Good Friday Agreement were held here.

4. The Royal Standard. The Union Flag flies when she is not present.

5. George III, who bought it as a private residence for his wife, Queen Charlotte.

6. He broke into Buckingham Palace and found his way into the Queen's very own bedroom where she was sleeping.

7. A: Prince Edward.

8. C: 775 rooms – including 188 staff bedrooms, 92 offices, 78 bathrooms, 52 royal and guest bedrooms and 19 state rooms.

9. James VI of Scotland and I of England.

10. The Macmillans. The Duchy of Cornwall purchased the house from the MP Maurice Macmillan who was the son of former Prime Minister Harold Macmillan.

11. B: £40 million.

12. Kensington Palace, which is currently the official London residence of the Duke and Duchess of Cambridge. In 1689 King William and Queen Mary commissioned Sir Christopher Wren to renovate and extend the original house to transform it into a royal palace.

13. Peter Pan.

14. The Prince of Wales and the Duchess of Cornwall.

15. A: £2.4 million.

16. The Isles of Scilly, off the Cornish coast, specifically on the island of St Mary's.

17. Gatcombe Park.

18. Balmoral Castle.

19. The Royal Mile.

20. Barrogill Castle, located in Caithness. The Queen Mother later restored its original name, the Castle of Mey.

Who Wore What, Where? Royal Fashion

1. Alexander McQueen. Kate Middleton had become aware of Burton's work in 2005, when she attended the wedding of the Duchess of Cornwall's son, Tom Parker Bowles. Burton had made the bride's dress. Kensington Palace stated that Kate opted for the Alexander McQueen house for her own dress because she admired the 'beauty of its craftmanship'.

2. Gloves (the company has held the royal warrant as the Queen's glovemaker since 1979). The Queen is thought to buy several dozen pairs of gloves each year, with each pair priced at a little over £100. However, she is known to then keep and wear favourite gloves for decades.

3. Beau Brummell. He perfected a look that incorporated full-length trousers (as opposed to knee breeches and stockings), beautifully tailored shirts, cravats and dark coats. However, Brummell struggled to finance his lifestyle and his wealthy friends began to desert him. Famously, on one occasion the Prince Regent pointedly ignored him and Brummell responded by gesturing towards him and asking a mutual acquaintance: 'Who's your fat friend?' From that moment, Brummell's social downfall was virtually complete.

4. By tradition, she should be married.

5. False. They designed Princess Diana's wedding dress. Princess Anne's dress was designed by Maureen Baker, chief designer for the Susan Small fashion label.

6. C: £81,100.01. This was despite the creation being uncharitably likened to a pretzel, a Turkey Twizzler and a toilet brush. The money was donated to Unicef and Children in Crisis.

7. Black (should mourning attire be needed).

Catherine Walker (born Catherine Marguerite Marie-Therese Baheux).

Wallis Blue. The shade was reportedly to match the colour of Ms Simpson's eyes.

Some observers claimed her hat – blue and dotted with yellow-centred flowers – bore a striking resemblance to the EU flag (which consists of gold stars on a blue background).

C: King Henry VIII.

The Duchess of Cambridge. Other royal *Vogue* covers have included Princess Anne and Princess Diana.

B: 10,000. The Sir Norman Hartnell designed dress was created from ivory silk that the Queen purchased using coupons, since rationing was still in operation. The design was inspired in part by Botticelli's *Allegory of Spring*.

Christina Stambolian.

Baby shawls. G.H. Hurt & Son is a Nottinghamshire-based family run company producing luxury knitted lace scarves and shawls.

Red. He wore the dress uniform of the Irish Guards, a regiment of which he was made colonel in February 2011.

Vogue editor-in-chief, Anna Wintour.

They are all milliners to the royal family.

The left. This leaves the right hand free for waving, shaking hands with dignitaries and so on.

Mario Testino. As well as portraits of the Prince of Wales, Prince William and Prince Harry, Testino also took the official engagement portraits of the Duke and Duchess of Cambridge.

The Art of Monarchy: Royalty and Culture

1. Andy Warhol.

2. Marilyn Monroe.

3. The Duke of Edinburgh.

4. B: Caravaggio. After Charles I was executed, Oliver Cromwell sold it but it was bought back into the Royal Collection by Charles II.

5. Cecil Beaton. Beaton was a long-time favourite of the Queen Mother and worked extensively with the royal family over the years. He won Oscars for his work on both *Gigi* and *My Fair Lady*.

6. *The Queen and I.*

7. Brian May, best known as the lead guitarist in, appropriately, the rock band Queen.

8. Lucian Freud.

9. Sherry. The tradition began in 1630 but fell away between 1800 and 1984, since when the sherry producers of Spain have provided a butt for each new appointee (equivalent to 720 bottles).

10. Carol Ann Duffy.

11. B: Princess Eugenie. Having earned a degree in art history, she joined the firm in 2015 and was promoted to director two years later.

12. Duke Ellington. Only one record was produced of the recording and it was only performed in public after Ellington's death in 1974.

13. Jack Vettriano – the portrait was titled *Olympia*.

14. The cello. Charles also had piano and trumpet lessons at school, although he described himself as 'awful'.

15. Hans Holbein the Younger. Henry VIII is sometimes credited with having dubbed Cleeves as a 'Flanders mare', but that description was not actually used until centuries later.

16. George Frideric Handel. It was originally commissioned for the coronation of George II.

17. Master of The Queen's Music. Office-holders originally directed the court orchestra, although these days the primary duty is to compose music for royal occasions. Judith Weir was appointed in 2015.

18. Anthony Blunt. He had admitted to being a member of the notorious Cambridge spy ring in the 1960s but his involvement was kept secret for a further 15 years.

19. The Sex Pistols.

20. Felix Mendelssohn. She made the observation in her diary on the occasion of his death in 1847.

Call That a Curtsy? Royal Protocol

1. A: Christmas Eve. This is a tradition that reflects the family's German heritage.

2. The US president, Donald Trump.

3. Queen Charlotte, consort of George III. The tradition was then more widely popularized by Victoria and Albert.

4. Windsor Castle.

5. 'Your Majesty'.

6. Patients diagnosed with the HIV virus.

7. 2015. This was when the 2013 Succession to the Crown Act came into effect. It ended the terms of the Royal Marriages Act 1772, which forbade anyone in the line of succession from marrying a Roman Catholic. (It had been legal to marry members of other religious faiths) The 2013 act also specified that only the first six in line to the throne must seek the monarch's approval for a marriage.

8. False. He was only present for the birth of Prince Edward.

9. True.

10. Prince William. Princess Diana gave birth to him in the Lindo Wing of St Mary's Hospital, London.

11. The prorogation of Parliament – in other words, the termination of a parliamentary session.

12. Maundy Money. The giving of Maundy Money by the monarch dates back to Edward II, with the granting of alms in the form of money meant to demonstrate the monarch's humility. (The tradition has its roots in the biblical story of Christ washing the feet of the disciples. Recipients used to be chosen for their poverty but are now usually nominated in recognition of service to their church or community.) Elizabeth decided early in her reign that the ceremony should not always be held in London, as had hitherto been the tradition, but should move to a different city each year. The value of the gift increases every year to reflect the monarch's increasing age.

13. Christmas puddings.

14. Myrtle.

15. True. The monarch is also the only person in the country who may drive legally without a valid licence.

16. C: Michelle Obama

17. True. She chose the ring from the Garrard jewellery collection. Traditionally, royal brides have opted for bespoke, handmade rings.

18. True. The tradition goes back to Queen Victoria, who considered that 'duke' was the fitting title for the holder of a dukedom regardless of sex, with 'duchess' serving as a courtesy title for a duke's consort.

19. 21. It is thought that the choice of 21 reflects old naval tradition. British naval ships customarily carried several guns and would announce their return to shore by firing them off. The land-based gunners were in the habit of returning three shots for each of the ship's one to welcome them back home, creating the blueprint for our modern 21-gun salute.

20. It should rhyme with 'jam'.

A Meal Fit for a King: What the Royals Eat and Drink

1. Gin and Dubonnet (a sweet, aromatic fortified wine).

2. She baked the Duke and Duchess of Cambridge's wedding cake – an eight-tier fruit cake.

3. The Palace of Whitehall, which was the main royal residence from 1530 to 1698.

4. C: 7 (Bollinger, Mumm & Cie, Krug, Laurent-Perrier, Louis Roederer, Moët & Chandon and Veuve Clicquot).

5. C: claret.

6. Four minutes.

7. Bendicks (of Mayfair).

8. It is a pig's head sewn on to the body of a capon and then roasted.

9. Earl Grey.

10. Beefeaters. The exact origins of the name are unclear. Some historians have linked it to the notion that they were previously part paid in meat. Another theory suggests that Henry VIII used his guards to test his food for fear of being poisoned. But perhaps most likely is that the name is derived from *beaufetiers*, an ancient term for a battle axe-wielding guard.

11. Edward VII (King Edward potatoes).

12. It was used to make the Queen's wedding cake in 1947. Sugar was still rationed in the UK at the time. The cake was nicknamed 'The 10,000 Mile Cake' as it incorporated ingredients sent from all over the world. In fact, the royal couple received 11 wedding cakes, with the official four-tiered, 2.75-metre-tall (9ft) one baked by the firm McVitie & Price.

13. A roast chicken.

14. Lunch.

15. Jam sandwiches cut to the size of an old penny coin.

16. Homemade chutney (made using her grandmother's recipe).

17. Balmoral Castle – the royal residence in Scotland.

18. C: 4,000.

19. Duchy Originals. Launching with its first product, the oaten biscuit, and the aim of supporting small- and medium-sized producers, it is now the UK's largest organic food and drink brand.

20. Coronation chicken, which is essentially chicken in a spiced mayonnaise sauce.

Planes, Trains and Carriages:
Royal Transport

1. *Gloriana*, which is 27 metre long (9ft).

2. A silver statuette of St George slaying the dragon.

3. A helicopter.

4. False. In fact, the Royal Collection numbers over 100.

5. The Glass Coach. Built in 1881 and designed as a sheriff's coach, it was purchased by the royal family ahead of George V's coronation in 1911. Elizabeth Bowes-Lyon was the first royal bride to use it on the occasion of her marriage to the future George VI in 1923.

6. The royal yacht *Britannia*.

7. Queen Victoria. On 13 June 1842, she travelled from Slough to Paddington in London behind an engine called Phlegethon.

8. Prince William. As a youngster, William was known to practise enthusiastically on a Kawasaki on his father's Highgrove estate.

9. False. He converted it to run on bioethanol fuel derived from wine. It apparently does about a mile for every four and a half bottles!

10. Bentley.

11. The two diesel locomotives used to pull the royal train. Prior to the Silver Jubilee in 1977, individual regions under the stewardship of British Rail each maintained rolling stock especially for use by the monarch and their family. In 1977, however, a single devoted train was kitted out for use anywhere on the network.

12. Air ambulances. In 2020 it was reported that he wanted to return to his former role during the Covid-19 pandemic.

13. Princess Beatrice. She was driving, while her bodyguard – also unhurt – sat in the passenger seat. The car was sandwiched between the two larger vehicles and suffered extensive damage.

14. Edward VII, who was driven in a Panhard Levassor in 1896 when he was the Prince of Wales.

15. George IV in 1821.

16. Edward, Prince of Wales (later Edward VIII), who took his first flight during the First World War (the exact date is disputed).

17. B: Phantom.

18. True. She learned as a member of the Women's Auxiliary Territorial Service of the British Army, which she joined in 1945.

19. Princess Diana (it was her first car, which she drove when she and Prince Charles were courting).

20. Concorde. The final commercial flight was between JFK International Airport, New York, and London Heathrow in 2003.

A Funny Thing Happened on the Way to Vanuatu: Royal Travels

<hr>

1. False. In fact, only the Queen has that right.

2. Canada, with Australia the second-most visited.

3. China. The visit was an indication of China's re-emergence on to the world stage after several decades of diplomatic isolation. The visit was considered particularly significant because the British and Chinese governments were at the time involved in intense negotiations concerning the handover of Hong Kong.

4. Canada. The couple soon moved again, though, this time setting up base in Los Angeles.

5. Sandringham House, Norfolk.

6. Richard I ('the Lionheart'), who reigned from 1189–99. The rest of the time was spent either on military expeditions or in captivity abroad.

7. South Africa. The couple took their baby son Archie on the ten-day tour that included an audience with Archbishop Desmond Tutu. Harry also made solo excursions to Angola, Botswana and Malawi.

8. Broadlands House. The couple spent the rest of their honeymoon at the Birkhall estate in Aberdeenshire.

9. Necker Island. Princess Diana first took William and Harry to the island in 1990, and Sarah Ferguson and Princesses Beatrice and Eugenie have also visited.

10. Thorpe Park.

11. Barley sugars.

12. The Taj Mahal in Agra, India – arguably the world's most spectacular monument to love.

13. Prince William, in 2018. The visit was considered an important staging post since the prince's presence was welcomed by both the warring Israeli and Palestinian authorities. Their conflict that had effectively ruled out any earlier official visit.

14. Harrods.

15. York. The journey took many weeks and was intended to consolidate the king's power after rumours emerged of a conspiracy against Henry in Yorkshire.

16. The Seychelles.

17. Mustique, a private Caribbean island.

18. A: yellow.

19. Kenya. She and Prince Philip were there on a brief break before embarking on an international tour that was scheduled to take in Australia and New Zealand.

20. The Republic of Ireland. The visit was important in marking the improved relations between the two countries some 13 years after the signing of the Good Friday Agreement that did much to end decades of violence over the question of Northern Irish sovereignty.

The Play's the Thing: Royalty on Stage and Screen

1. *Coronation Street*. Charles is seen visiting the fictional Weatherfield Town Hall.

2. Helen Mirren.

3. C: Zara and Mike Tindall. The former rugby star narrowly won!

4. Alan Bennett.

5. Prunella Scales.

6. *Suits*.

7. Wayne Sleep. Diana's performance was a surprise for Prince Charles's birthday.

8. True. Her mother, Sarah, Duchess of York, also had a production credit on the movie.

9. A: *The Audience*.

10. The Lord Chamberlain's Men. The company was founded in 1594 under the patronage of Henry Carey, the then Lord Chamberlain, but came under the new king's patronage in 1603.

11. Bluebottle.

12. Elizabeth I (in 1998's *Elizabeth* and 2007's *Elizabeth: The Golden Age*).

13. Ardent Productions. The company produced a number of dramas and factual programmes, including a well-received documentary on Edward VIII, but was wound up in 2009.

14. Prince Harry.

15. *Richard II*. The words are spoken by John of Gaunt, son of Edward III, on his deathbed.

16. Camilla, Duchess of Cornwall. Princess Margaret had previously appeared in the same show back in 1984.

17. George VI. The film focuses on George's true-life struggle to execute his public role while struggling with a speech impediment.

18. *The Crown*. Foy played Elizabeth II as a young woman, Coleman in her mid-years, with Imelda Staunton taking on the role as Elizabeth approached older age.

19. The Windsors.

20. *Shakespeare in Love*. She received the Academy Award for Best Supporting Actress in 1999.

Not on the Carpet! Royal Pets

1. True. The dogs are fed from porcelain bowls, delivered to them by the butler!

2. B: Carl Fabergé. Known as the 'Sandringham Commission', it most famously includes a statue of Edward's favourite dog, Caesar, adorned with rubies and gold. In real life, Caesar wore a collar that read, 'I belong to the king'.

3. Zara Tindall. Princess Anne's daughter rode Toytown on the international eventing circuit for many years before the horse's retirement in 2011. Toytown could be a difficult horse on occasions but the pair achieved a number of titles and podium finishes.

4. C: an English cocker spaniel.

5. B: a cat. Cali is a Siamese.

6. A: a cheetah.

7. Battersea Dogs Home. Queen Victoria became its first royal patron after her son Leopold adopted Skippy, a fox terrier, in 1882.

8. True. The hound hitched a lift with Her Majesty to Windsor shortly before the nuptials.

9. Queen Victoria. Dash was her most beloved spaniel.

10. Catherine of Aragon.

11. Charles II (the King Charles spaniel). Charles was not the first British monarch to own examples of these dogs but his particular fondness for them cemented their popularity, earning the breed its name. He allowed his spaniels to roam freely around Whitehall Palace, while Samuel Pepys even noted in his diary the king's playfulness around them.

12. A: a pair of pygmy hippos, intended as a gift for the young Prince Andrew. The creatures were subsequently regifted to Whipsnade Zoo.

13. A bear cub, which subsequently lived in London Zoo. The Soviet leader gifted the animal during a visit to Britain.

14. False. However, Mary, Queen of Scots did. After she was beheaded in 1587, her Skye terrier reportedly appeared from beneath her skirts where he had been secreted.

15. A crocodile. The baby animal was a gift from the people of Berending, a village on the River Gambia, and was presented in a silver biscuit tin.

16. Princess Anne. She pleaded guilty to the charge in 2002 and paid a fine. In doing so, she became the first royal to attend court in over a century.

17. A: an African elephant.

18. A: a polar bear.

19. She was bitten while breaking up a fight among several of her dogs.

20. True. Legend has it that Margaret was particularly keen on placing the reptile on a favourite book and watching it turn red to match the cover.

A Day at the Races: The Royals and Sport

1. A polo match. The event was hosted at Windsor Great Park.

2. B: the Aga Khan.

3. Marylebone Cricket Club (the MCC).

4. The Queen's jockeys' sport a purple body with gold braid and scarlet sleeves, plus a black velvet cap with gold fringe.

5. Aston Villa.

6. Usain Bolt.

7. False, but she did name one of her horses Charlton after the 1966 World Cup-winning siblings, Bobby and Jackie.

8. BBC Sport's Personality of the Year.

9. B: a pigeon.

10. The Invictus Games. The games were first held in London in 2014.

11. C: Sailing.

12. Captain Mark Phillips.

13. A: sex testing.

14. Stanley Matthews. Matthews is regarded as one of the all-time greats of the British game. Playing for Stoke City and Blackpool, he represented England in two World Cups, was named European Footballer of the Year in 1956 and was still playing in the English top divisions when in his 50s.

15. Mike Tindall. The couple met during the 2003 Rugby World Cup in Australia. They married on 30 July 2011 at the Canongate Kirk in Edinburgh, Scotland.

16. Devon Loch.

17. Klosters. Charles first visited in 1978, and in 2018 he even hosted a private party to mark his 40-year association with the resort.

18. C: Carriage driving.

19. Roger Federer. The duchess made the revelation to Britain's Fed Cup captain, Anne Keothavong.

20. A parachute. In fact, the Queen was played by stuntman Gary Connery sporting a wig.

A Family Affair: Royal Family Connections

1. Camilla, Duchess of Cornwall.

2. They were first cousins, sharing a set of grandparents.

3. George W. Bush.

4. Peter Phillips, the son of Princess Anne and Captain Mark Phillips, born 15 November 1977.

5. Three (Edward VI, Mary and Elizabeth I).

6. Sophie Winkleman.

7. Guy Ritchie.

8. Charles. The 9th Earl Spencer was Diana's younger brother by three years.

9. Edward VII (although he was yet to ascend the throne when Albert Victor died in 1892 aged 28, the victim of an influenza pandemic).

10. Spencer Matthews, who rose to fame in the show *Made in Chelsea*. Pippa is married to his hedge-fund-running brother, James Matthews.

11. He was her grandson. Victoria's eldest daughter, also called Victoria, had married Prince Frederick William of Prussia (later Emperor Frederick III) and Wilhelm was their son. Victoria had 42 grandchildren, earning her the nickname 'the Grandmother of Europe'.

12. King Harald V of Norway. Harald and Elizabeth are second cousins, and at the time of his birth Harald was 16th in line to the throne.

13. Gordonstoun, in Moray, Scotland.

14. Caroline of Brunswick. The couple had separated in 1796 but Caroline returned to England for the coronation to assert her right to be recognized as queen consort. Caroline fell ill and died less than three weeks after the ceremony.

15. He is a first cousin.

16. Mountbatten, a family surname on his mother's side.

17. B: Grandpa England

18. Saxe-Coburg-Gotha. The king decided to 'rebrand' the house amid high levels of anti-German sentiment.

19. Ralph Fiennes. Fiennes can trace his family line back to James II of Scotland.

20. Barbara McCorquodale – better known as Dame Barbara Cartland – one of the world's best-selling romantic novelists.

We Are a Bit Amused: Royal Quirks

1. True. And it is for the entirely sensible reason that it is always on hand in case of a medical emergency.

2. True. The Groom of the Stool was an ancient position and may have originally involved such tasks as wiping the monarchical bottom. However, by the Tudor era, it had evolved into a role of national significance, the holder being more concerned with the ruler's financial outgoings than their bowel movements!

3. B: the River Jordan, where Jesus was baptized by John the Baptist.

4. False. She does, though, prefer 'ice balls' to cubes.

5. False, but Elizabeth I did. Also banned in the edict were the use of false hair and high-heeled shoes.

6. C: the Grand Carver, whose duties include carving the monarch's meat at official functions.

7. True. At the State Opening of Parliament attended by the Queen, it is traditional for representatives of the Royal Household to 'take a parliamentary hostage' (usually one of the government's whips), who is held at Buckingham Palace until the monarch's safe return. The tradition dates to the time of Charles I, but nowadays is purely symbolic.

8. True. Attenborough believed the royals would regret allowing the film, called *Royal Family*, to dent the mystique that surrounded them. Indeed, the Queen has refused permission for the film to be broadcast in full again since 1972.

9. A: a place of worship under the direct control of the monarch, rather than a bishop. Royal peculiars include Westminster Abbey, the Chapel Royal at St James's Palace, St George's Chapel in Windsor Castle and the Savoy Chapel in London.

10. Ravens. Legend has it that disaster would befall the kingdom were the ravens to abandon the Tower.

11. Henry VIII. He demanded the peculiar measure as a protection against any of his staff smearing poison on his bed linen.

12. George III. George's struggles with his mental health are well documented and this particular rumour, the veracity of which is uncertain, formed part of the narrative of his battle.

13. True. At the time the Queen came to the throne, succession to the monarchy was on a system of male-preference primogeniture. In other words, a son always trumped a daughter even if they were born later. The law was only repealed in 2013 to a system of absolute primogeniture, so that the line of succession for those born since 2011 works on an age-only basis, regardless of gender.

14. Elizabeth I. She contracted a near fatal bout of smallpox when she was 29 years old. Among her other make-up habits, she customarily used vermilion – powdered cinnabar containing mercury – to give colour to her cheeks and lips.

15. B: garlic. In contrast, she is known to be particularly partial to mangoes and chocolate.

16. B: James I – although the good doctor did make a proviso that since 'the king hates eating human bodies, an ox's head can be substituted in his case'.

17. *Macbeth* – specifically for the scenes involving the three witches.

18. A: wear a hat in the presence of the monarch. The legal foundation of the privilege is, nonetheless, disputed.

19. C: a single daffodil. The flowers are an important agricultural product of the islands.

20. False. However, they may claim any dolphin, whale or sturgeon – a right codified by a statute of 1324, enacted in the reign of Edward II.

What a Way to Go: Royal Deaths

1. Richard III, at the Battle of Bosworth Field in 1485.

2. He was the chauffeur of her car when it crashed in Paris in 1997.

3. Edmund II (also known as Edmund Ironside). Edmund had been engaged in a long battle with the Danish forces of King Cnut when he died. The historian Henry of Huntingdon (c. 1088–c. 1157) claimed Edmund died in this grisly way, and it is certainly possible that he was murdered. However, other contemporaries made no mention of this particular method of 'dethronement', blaming disease or battle wounds instead.

4. Two. Anne Boleyn was beheaded on 19 May 1536 on charges that included adultery, incest (with her brother) and plotting to kill the king – at least some of the charges were entirely trumped up. Catherine Howard was then beheaded on 13 February 1542, without a trial, on the grounds of treason relating to allegations of having been pre-contracted to marry Frances Dereham before she married Henry, and for conducting a relationship with Thomas Culpeper while queen.

5. Too much fish. Records show he died from 'a surfeit of' lampreys, a fish that is a little like an eel.

6. Paris. He died on 28 May 1972, after a battle with throat cancer.

7. B: Charles II – referring to his most beloved mistress, Nell Gwynne.

8. Her beloved Scottish servant, John Brown.

9. King John. John faced an uprising from his unhappy barons and was retreating from his enemies when he fell ill. The Wash was notoriously boggy and his luggage train, including his Crown Jewels, was caught in rising waters.

10. Henry VIII. Just how true this story is has long been debated by historians. However, it seems likely that embalmers were slow to get to work on his corpse because of an immediate desire to keep his death secret, during which time, it has been suggested, there could have been a build up of gases that led to the Sion Abbey incident.

11. Mary, Queen of Scots. She was executed on 8 February 1587. A Catholic, Mary was considered a threat to the English throne of her Protestant cousin, Elizabeth I, and was ultimately found guilty of plotting to assassinate her.

12. False. It was actually 'Hyde Park Corner'. The code was used to preserve discretion among the various individuals and agencies concerned with planning the royal funeral – an activity done far in advance of the event itself.

13. Leicester.

14. C: Malmsey wine (a type of fortified wine, like Madeira).

15. Harold Godwinson. Harold was involved in a three-way struggle for the English Crown that involved not only his enemy at Hastings, William of Normandy, but also the Norwegian king, Harald Hardrada. Godwinson had defeated Hardrada at the Battle of Stamford Bridge just three weeks before the Battle of Hastings, which proved a step too far for his forces.

16. George V. The king had battled poor health for many years, and the death of his sister, Victoria, in December 1935 took its toll, too. On 20 January 1936, his physicians issued a statement confirming that 'The king's life is moving peacefully towards its close' – but the question remains as to whether its end was hastened more than the law was comfortable with.

17. Charles I.

18. Edward V and Richard, Duke of York.

19. Prince George, Duke of Kent (son of George V and brother of George VI).

20. Louis Mountbatten, 1st Earl Mountbatten of Burma.

Snog, Marry, Avoid: Royal Love Lives

1. Ulrika Jonsson. The Swedish-born model and presenter made the claim in 2010, ending decades of speculation that the pair had been 'an item' in the late 1980s.

2. Photographer. The Earl of Snowdon remained a noted photographer throughout his life (he died in 2017) and also branched out into filmmaking.

3. Princess Beatrice. She had been scheduled to marry property developer Edoardo Mapelli Mozzi.

4. True. In 1785, he married Maria Fitzherbert in a ceremony that was illegal on two scores – she was a Roman Catholic so could not then marry an heir to the throne, and George had failed to get the necessary permission to wed from his father. Fitzherbert was, nonetheless, the love of George's life and she considered herself his true wife even when he married again ten years later.

5. Princess Eugenie. Her husband, Jack Brooksbank, worked at the club earlier in his career in hospitality and is now a brand ambassador for George Clooney's tequila brand, Casamigos.

6. Twice. She divorced naval pilot Earl Winfield Spencer Jr in 1927 and shipbroker Ernest Simpson in 1937. She was in the process of divorcing her second husband at the time of the abdication crisis.

7. John Bryan. The affair between the duchess and the financial advisor was not to be long-lived. Bryan was declared bankrupt in 1996 and married a Belgian reality television star 28 years his junior in 2006, but the couple were involved in a highly publicized divorce seven years later.

8. Mollie King.

9. Andrew Parker Bowles, ex-husband of the Duchess of Cornwall. He rode his horse The Fossa to an 11th-place finish.

10. Peter and Autumn Phillips. The couple were, however, seen together at the Cheltenham Festival just a few weeks later.

11. 'Squidgy' – as a result of which the episode came to be known as 'Squidgygate'.

12. Sir Timothy Laurence. Anne met him, a naval officer, while he was serving as an equerry to the Queen in the 1980s.

13. Elizabeth Woodville. Elizabeth was considered a highly unsuitable candidate for royal marriage – five years older than the king, she was also a Lancastrian (arch enemies of Edward's Yorkist supporters) and had already been married to a relatively lowly Lancastrian knight. She was, however, a noted beauty and won the king's heart. The couple went on to have ten children together.

14. Koo Stark. Her appearance in *Emily*, which contained a number of explicit scenes, was regarded by some observers as a key reason that the couple were pressurized to end their relationship.

15. B: Captain Mark Phillips was revealed as the father of her child, which was the result of an affair in 1984.

16. Mary. It has even been rumoured that Henry fathered two children by her, although there is little in the way of concrete proof.

17. Edward VII. Langtry was his paramour while he was still the Prince of Wales.

18. Captain Peter Townsend. There was significant opposition to the union in royal circles on the grounds that marriage to a divorcee contravened the rules of the Church of England, of which her sister was head.

19. A: Philip. She called him 'Philip Charles Arthur George' instead of 'Charles Philip Arthur George'

20. True. Harry arranged a private tour of the museum at a time when it was closed to all other visitors.

Annus Horribilis: Royal Scandal and Strife

1. 1992. The year included much-publicized problems in the marriages of Prince Charles, Princess Anne and Prince Andrew, the suicide of her nephew, Prince Albrecht of Hohenlohe-Langenburg and a devastating fire at Windsor Castle.

2. King James I. Fawkes and his co-conspirators were Roman Catholics, while James was a Protestant.

3. The Fake Sheikh – real name, Mazher Mahmood. Mahmood was subsequently imprisoned for conspiring to pervert the course of justice in relation to another sting operation.

4. A swastika armband (and an eagle) as part of what appeared to be a Nazi uniform. He wore the offending outfit to a party at Highgrove House.

5. Henry Stuart, Lord Darnley. Mary's third husband, the Earl of Bothwell, was widely suspected of being responsible for the death.

6. The Duchess of Cambridge. She was staying in a private holiday home when the photos were taken.

7. B: He stole Queen Victoria's underwear, along with other royal paraphernalia, during a crime spree that saw him break into Buckingham Palace three times.

8. Pippa Middleton. She was referring to the worldwide media interest in her behind that resulted from her appearance as her sister's bridesmaid in 2011.

9. Prince William. A film crew was accused of contravening industry guidelines on royal privacy while filming at the prince's university. The following year, Edward stood down from his senior role with the company.

10. Epilepsy. It has been suggested that his isolation was in part to stymie public knowledge of his illness for fear that such knowledge would be detrimental to the monarchy's standing.

11. Jeffrey Epstein. The prince fiercely denied having knowledge of Epstein's crimes at the time when they associated with each other.

12. Chris Tarrant. At the time, the two were colleagues at Capital Radio, where Sophie worked in public relations.

13. C: cherry brandy. Charles claimed it was hitherto the only alcoholic drink he had tried, having been given a tot by his mother. His drink in the pub cost him two shillings and sixpence, not to mention a lot of tabloid scrutiny.

14. B: She was one of his teachers at Eton, where she claimed she was told to ghostwrite a project for him. She made the allegations, dating to 2004, in a tribunal for her claim of unfair dismissal against the school. The tribunal ruled there was no evidence that Harry had cheated but did recognize that he had received help. Her legal case was subsequently settled.

15. Charles II. The fire broke out in 1666.

16. Roddy Llewellyn – with whom she had begun what would be an eight-year affair three years earlier.

17. Princess Anne. The attempted abduction occurred when her car was forced to stop by another vehicle. When her armed assailant ordered her to go with him, she responded: 'Not bloody likely!' The attacker was subsequently overpowered and arrested. He pleaded guilty to attempted murder and kidnap and was detained under the Mental Health Act.

18. 'Her Royal Highness'. Prince William was said to have pledged to return it to her when he ascended to the throne.

19. To her father, Thomas Markle. She sent the missive in the fraught build-up to her wedding in 2018.

20. A: Abdul Karim (the movie was *Victoria & Abdul*). Karim became a firm favourite of the queen, to the dissatisfaction of prominent figures within the Royal Household. After Victoria's death in 1901, Karim was returned to India at the behest of Edward VII, and most of the correspondence between the queen and her attendant was burned.

Tabloid Tittle-Tattle: Royal Rumours

1. True. She regularly assisted staff in capturing and releasing pipistrelle bats that nested in the rafters of the Balmoral ballroom.

2. False. Edward's love of treading the boards is well documented (especially from his university days) but he has not tried to get a spot on the show whose winner gets to appear at the Royal Variety Performance.

3. True.

4. True, according to evidence provided by Princess Diana's former butler, Paul Burrell in a television documentary. He also claimed the prince has someone squeeze his toothpaste on to his toothbrush. Charles has not, however, commented on the claims.

5. False. Zara has appeared on the show – as have her husband and mother over the years – but she has not turned down the position of team captain, nor has the Queen ever moved to block family members from appearing.

6. Sadly for the royal coffers, this is false. Members of the royal family are well known for their love of racing. The Queen Mother, for instance, took *The Sporting Life* each day. Nonetheless, there is no evidence for Anne's particular prowess in predicting winners, despite her own skills as a horse rider.

7. True. The scar resulted from a childhood golfing mishap, and William himself has likened it to the one Harry Potter sports.

8. True. It was his early attempt to pronounce 'Granny'.

9. True. Harry challenged the Olympian during a fateful night in Las Vegas that culminated with Harry being photographed naked in a hotel room (an event at which Lochte was not present) – pictures that subsequently were published around the world.

10. False. But she does have staff to break in new shoes for her.

11. True. He did so during a surprise concert for the Duchess of Cornwall's 60th birthday.

12. False. This is a much-touted rumour but Charles suggested it was nonsense during a radio interview in Australia in 2018.

13. False. The prince has maintained a high level of physical fitness into old age, thanks in part to a healthy diet and his devotion to exercise (notably a regime used by the Canadian Air Force). But he has not taken on the famous strong man in an eating contest. Yet...

14. True. The design was based on the city's iconic hire bikes.

15. False, although that was the case until a law change in 1998. However, it is still an offence to eat the birds under the 1981 Wildlife and Countryside Act.

16. True. A section of the populace on the island of Tanna, part of the nation of Vanuatu, venerate the prince as a deity.

17. False, but he was tattooed with a dragon and a tiger on a trip to Japan in 1881. It is thought that George's father, the then Prince of Wales (the future King Edward VII), gave his blessing to the scheme. The Prince of Wales had a tattoo of his own, a Jerusalem Cross inked on a visit to the Holy Land.

18. This is, alas, false, although she did inspect it on a trip to the show's Northern Ireland set in 2014. It was reported that the Queen declined the opportunity as tradition disbars her from sitting on any foreign throne!

19. False, but she appeared in 34 episodes of the show as 'Briefcase Model No. 24'. 'I would put that in the category of things I was doing when I was trying to make ends meet', she later commented.

20. Extraordinarily, this is true! The incident happened on a players' night out during their ill-fated tournament.

Celebrity Friends: Royal Connections
to the Rich and Famous

1. Danny Dyer.

2. Ed Sheeran. However, Blunt later revealed that he and Sheeran had fabricated the story.

3. Rose Arbuthnot-Leslie.

4. Duran Duran. In 1983, the princess met the band backstage when they appeared at a Prince's Trust Rock Gala in London.

5. Caroline Flack.

6. Usain Bolt. In fact, the prince is thought to have held a fairly restrained stag event in the Scottish Highlands.

7. Eddie Redmayne. The pair were rugby teammates, too.

8. A: Alexander Graham Bell – the Scot–American telephone pioneer. The two met when Bell provided a demonstration of his invention.

9. Serena Williams.

10. B: Coldplay.

11. *The Grand Knockout Tournament* (also known as *It's a Royal Knockout*). The show was based on the popular knock-about entertainment show, *It's a Knockout* and was a passion project of Prince Edward. However, the response to the show from within Buckingham Palace, and from the world at large, was lukewarm. In fact, Edward stormed out of a press conference when his question to journalists, 'Well, what did you think?', met with a muted response.

12. **B: Hilary Duff.** One of her 17th-century ancestors was a 10th great-grandson of Edward III.

13. **Cressida Bonas.** The pair remained on good terms after their split and Bonas was a guest at Harry's wedding in 2018.

14. **Elton John.** Diana and Elton John were friends and Diana had agreed to write a foreword to Versace's book, profits from which were to go to John's charity. However, Diana pulled out of the project late on, probably owing to the risqué nature of some of the book's content.

15. **David Attenborough.**

16. **Ellie Goulding.** The multi-award-winning performer was already on friendly terms with the young royals prior to her performance.

17. **Victoria and David Beckham.**

18. **Dame Emma Thompson.** William politely refused!

19. **John Lennon.**

20. **Geri Halliwell** (Ginger Spice of the Spice Girls).

What Are You Talking About? Quotations By and About the Royal Family

<hr>

1. A: Britney Spears. She made the claim on *The Frank Skinner Show* in 2002, suggesting that shortly after being 'stood up' she began dating Justin Timberlake.

2. Charles I (in his 1628 Declaration on the Dissolution of Parliament).

3. Martin Bashir. In that interview, Diana explored her husband's and her own infidelities, her struggles with her mental health and the question of Charles's suitability to rule. It was, all in all, the death knell for their marriage.

4. C: a firm.

5. Donald Trump, speaking after his state visit to the UK in 2019.

6. Meghan Markle.

7. Edward VIII. He made the statement in a broadcast confirming his abdication so that he might marry Wallis Simpson.

8. The National Gallery in London.

9. Nasa's Apollo 11 mission to land a man on the moon.

10. Prince Harry.

11. Queen Victoria.

12. If she was 'okay'? Bradbury was enquiring how she had coped through pregnancy and as a new mum under the intense media glare that goes with being a royal.

13. Spike Milligan. Charles is famously a fan of The Goons, of whom Milligan was an integral member.

14. In the Woking branch of Pizza Express.

15. The Queen Mother. The Queen made the observation in a broadcast to the nation shortly after her mother's death.

16. The great church reformist, Martin Luther.

17. George V.

18. Tony Blair, who was addressing the nation as prime minister. A couple of years earlier, Diana herself had given an interview in which she said: 'I'd like to be a queen in people's hearts.'

19. B: John Travolta. The pair were attendees at a gala dinner hosted by President Reagan and they danced to music from Travolta's 1977 movie, *Saturday Night Fever*.

20. Niagara Falls.

Long to Reign Over Us: Royal Firsts and Other Records

1. William IV. He came to the throne on 26 June 1830 and reigned until his death on 20 June 1837. Prince Charles, however, seems one day destined to break his record by some distance.

2. C: Princess Beatrice, who ran the race on behalf of a number of children's charities.

3. C: 83

4. Edward IV, who measured in at 1.94 metres (a little over 6ft 4in).

5. Victoria, at 1.52 metres (just shy of 5ft).

6. George VI who, with his wife Elizabeth, crossed the Canadian border to Niagara Falls in New York State in 1939.

7. James VI of Scotland and I of England, in 1603.

8. Edward I (1239–1307). His first wife, Eleanor of Castile, gave birth to at least 14 children, and his second wife, Margaret of France, bore him a further three. Meanwhile, George III (1738–1820) also came close with 15 legitimate children of his own.

9. B: Collen took the first photograph of a British monarch. Photography in the UK was really born around 1839, when Henry Fox Talbot introduced the British public to the new art form. Victoria and Albert were early fans and Collen, hitherto better known as a painter of miniatures, snapped the queen and her daughter Victoria in a double portrait.

10. A flush toilet, although Elizabeth was apparently no great fan of the noisy invention.

11. A: stockings.

12. Rudyard Kipling. The speech acknowledged the technological developments that made the broadcast possible before focusing on the need to work towards peace and encouraging people to aim for 'prosperity without self-seeking'. The broadcast garnered an estimated audience of 20 million people.

13. B: Princess Margaret and Antony Armstrong-Jones. They were married in 1960.

14. False. James II of England and VII of Scotland was deemed by Parliament to have abdicated when he fled to France during the Glorious Revolution of 1688. Mary, Queen of Scots was also forced to abdicate the Scottish throne in 1567.

15. George (of whom there have been six in total).

16. Prince Charles, who studied history, archaeology and anthropology at Trinity College, Cambridge, between 1967 and 1970.

17. Mary I, who came to the throne in July 1553 after the death of her brother, Edward VI, and was crowned in October that year.

18. C: 1967.

19. Edward of Carnarvon, son of Edward I and Eleanor of Castile, who was made Prince of Wales in 1301 and then reined as Edward II from 1307 until 1327.

20. Edward VII. He was born on 9 November 1841 and died on 6 May 1910.

1066 and All That: Famous Dates in Royal History

1. The second Saturday of June.

2. Princess Anne. For the record, Charles was born 14 November 1948, Andrew 19 February 1960 and Edward 10 March 1964.

3. William I (William the Conqueror) in 1066.

4. 2005. They were married in a civil ceremony at Windsor Guildhall, followed by a reception at Windsor Castle.

5. She was named their 'Woman of the Year'.

6. 2015. Princess Charlotte of Cambridge celebrates her birthday on 2 May.

7. The 1550s. The exact date was 15 January 1559.

8. 2002.

9. 1936 (George V died, Edward VIII abdicated and George VI ascended to the throne).

10. 1953.

11. The 1740s – 1743 to be precise. The battle, part of the War of the Austrian Succession, was a victory for the Allied forces of Britain, Hanover and Austria.

12. 1837.

13. A: Prince Charles.

14. 1215. The charter of rights, signed at Runnymead near Windsor, was designed to repair the crumbling relations between John and his barons. In fact, it paved the way for constitutional freedoms that continue to underpin key aspects of modern democracy.

15. 1986.

16. B: 1649. 1642 marked the start of the English Civil War that culminated in the king's execution seven years later. After the unhappy spell of Oliver Cromwell's Protectorate, Charles's son, Charles II, returned to claim the throne in 1660.

17. Princess Beatrice.

18. C: 1688.

19. A teenager fired six blank shots from a pistol at the Queen. She was, thankfully, unhurt.

20. 1851. The exhibition, which showcased British and international design and innovation, was based in South Kensington, London, and led on to the establishment of the V&A Museum.

A Royal Rummage

1. B: Lilibet.

2. Prince Charles. Her own father did not attend the ceremony, having suffered health problems shortly beforehand.

3. Tony Blair. He was born on 6 May 1953 – so just over a month before her coronation – and served as prime minister from 1997 to 2007.

4. Elizabeth I, addressing English troops awaiting the arrival of the Spanish Armada in 1588.

5. The Queen was born there, at number 17.

6. Denmark.

7. They were the Queen's bridesmaids.

8. Clare Waight Keller, the artistic director of the Givenchy fashion house. The Duchess of Sussex said she 'wanted to highlight the success of a leading British talent'. A piece of blue fabric from the dress she wore on her first date with Prince Harry was discreetly sewn into her veil.

9. Caernarfon Castle.

10. Wales, in recognition of his father's royal title.

11. Elizabeth I. The conditions were detailed in the 1562 Articles for the Execution of the Statutes of Apparel, although most of them were subsequently repealed by James I.

12. *Country Life* magazine.

13. B: Football boots. He is thought to be the first known owner of a pair, although they likely held little resemblance to the boots we know today.

14. True. The corporation judged that to have broadcast comedy in the circumstances would have been disrespectful.

15. False. They are emblazoned with a crown, while other members of the royal family make do with a coronet.

16. False. The Queen did not attend school but was educated at home by private tutors.

17. Football. Back in 1314, Edward II had also attempted to ban the game on account of the raucousness it provoked. There were further decrees against the sport by Edward IV, Richard II and Henry IV.

18. Nicholas Witchell, a journalist and broadcaster who had become the BBC's royal correspondent. He had incurred the wrath of the palace back in 2002 with an obituary of Princess Margaret that was considered unflattering and had just asked Prince William a question about his father's forthcoming marriage to Camilla Parker Bowles when Charles made his comment.

19. A piper.

20. Alexandra Mary.

First published in Great Britain in 2020 by

Greenfinch
An imprint of Quercus Editions Ltd
Carmelite House
50 Victoria Embankment
London EC4Y 0DZ

An Hachette UK company

A CIP catalogue record for this book is available from the British Library

HB ISBN 978-1-52941-046-4
Ebook ISBN 978-1-52941-047-1

10 9 8 7 6 5 4 3 2 1

Designed by Nathan Burton
Cover images: Shutterstock.com. Front: Atlas Studio; Back: Oksanast
Interior artwork: Andrew Pinder
Printed and bound in Great Britain by Clays

Papers used by Quercus Editions Ltd are from well-managed forests and
other responsible sources.